THE
STRANGER
AT THE
WINDOW

THE
STRANGER
AT THE
WINDOW

Guy McElveny

BREWIN BOOKS

First published by
Brewin Books Ltd, 56 Alcester Road,
Studley, Warwickshire B80 7LG in 2015
www.brewinbooks.com

ISBN: 978-1-85858-549-9

A Cataloguing in Publication Record
for this title is available from the British Library.

Typeset in Agmena Pro Book
Printed in Great Britain
by Bell & Bain Ltd.

Part I:

January 1944

1

I was eighteen that winter – that was the point when my life changed completely. It was January 1944; I had just been called up for the navy and was waiting for a ship. Geoffrey was a year older than me – he was already serving in the airforce. That day, he had come home on leave, as he did every six weeks, and as always, I'd set off early to meet him at the station. The year that separated us had seemed like a lifetime while we were growing up, but I had finally caught up with him, though not in a way I had foreseen: I would also be leaving home sometime in the new year, and I knew how hard it would be for Mother with both of us away.

Whenever he came home on leave, we used to go drinking together and then to the dances at Thimblemill Baths. They didn't use it much for swimming in the war as far as I can remember; most of the time, the pool was drained and boarded over with a wooden dance floor. It always amazed me to see it transformed in that way: to see all the outward signs of a swimming baths – the spectators' balconies, the green and orange tiles – and then to see it being used for dancing.

I can still remember the atmosphere of those nights, the feeling of excitement and anticipation: Geoff would always be walking ahead of me, cigarette smoke pouring over his shoulder, as if he was in a hurry. 'Get a move on or we'll miss it,' he kept saying. There was always a crowd of girls around him at the dance – he was very handsome in his blue airman's uniform – but he preferred drinking to dancing. One night, he tried to smuggle a girl into the house, but he couldn't get the key in the door and he woke everyone up; he was laughing and Mother was shaking her head and saying 'You're drunk again!' – she was absolutely furious. Father took it all in good humour and offered to take the girl home, but Geoff refused to believe he was drunk; he was talking in a booming voice, as if this would keep him sober: 'I'll walk her home – no problem.'

'Yes, if you can stand up,' said Mother, and we waited while he staggered out to the toilet by the coalhouse. It was then that we heard a loud crash from the garden. He had fallen over and banged his head on something; he had a nasty cut above the eye, but he was still laughing. He'd always been more outgoing than me and he liked to enjoy himself, so I thought nothing of it at the time, but later it crossed my mind that he drank because he was scared.

2

Shivering, head down against the icy blasts of wind, I made my way out to the shed at the bottom of the garden. The sheet of tarpaulin that covered the entrance to our Anderson shelter had come loose and was snapping like the sail of a ship.

I found the chicken hanging from a hook behind the door: still warm, its feathers bright and unmatted – I half expected it to start squawking and flapping about.

But Father used to wring their necks and its head swung limply as I took it down. It was my job to pluck the bird – that evening, Mother was preparing a special meal for Geoffrey's homecoming.

It was thanks to Father's efforts in the garden – and Mother's in the kitchen – that we were able to enjoy that kind of meal once in a while. As well as keeping chickens, the old man had become a dab hand at growing vegetables. Gardening was his passion – he used to grow the most amazing flowers you ever saw: there were pink and white peonies, which my mother adored, and white and purple lupins. But that was a long time ago; when the war started, we had spent an entire Saturday – just the two of us armed with pitchforks and spades – turning over the lawn and flowerbeds. We composted the lot and put in vegetables: carrots and potatoes at first, then cabbages, onions and beetroot – the old man's favourite.

It made me sad to see him destroy that garden – all those months of effort gone in a few hours – but he went about the task stoically: bent over his spade, Woodbine dangling from his mouth. He spent most of his spare time working in the garden, staying out till all hours; Mother would often have to call him in long after it got dark.

When it became too cold for gardening, he could usually be found in his shed working on his latest creation. He was the most ingenious man I ever met; he would bring home bits of scrap metal from the workshop – he was a tool-maker by trade – and make something for the house or garden – amazing things, things no one else could have dreamt up. He made his own moulds – I'm not sure how – and had cast a team of miniature cricket players out of plaster and arranged them in the garden: one had a bat and there was a ball suspended in mid-air on an invisible wire. One Christmas, to amuse me and my brother, he made a cow out of wire and papier mâché – it must have taken him hours. It was almost lifesize and it looked like the real thing – he had even painted the markings on it. It had a rubber glove for an udder and you could actually milk the cow. On Christmas morning, he dressed up as a milkmaid in one of Mother's old dresses and put on a wig with plaits. Mother wasn't amused and she shouted at him: 'Where do you think we're going to put that?' But Geoffrey and I loved it.

My father had a greenhouse just next to the house and a sunken shed at the bottom of the garden; it had window lights in the roof, but the roof was flat and you couldn't see it from the house. I can still remember the smell of that shed – of creosote, damp earth and leaves. He showed me one day how to make a flame appear as if by magic. He wiped the mildew and grime from the window, letting through the rays of sunlight, and then placed a magnifying glass at a slant, propped in the claw of the hammer. He set some newspaper beneath it and I watched as slowly, the paper began to yellow, then to smoulder before bursting into flame. He was always doing things like that; they seemed incredible to me, like the time he made a telephone out of tobacco tins and wire so we could send messages from the house to the shed.

I think Father was a true artist: these days somebody would probably recognize his talent. My mother often encouraged him to go for the job of foreman, but he would say gently, 'No, Mary', and in the end she stopped asking. He was offered the position on a number of occasions, but always turned it down. Mother was furious when she found out – she would have liked the extra money – but he was happy where he was, working with his hands.

My mother could appear stern to people who didn't know her, but she was very loving towards all of us. She was a fantastic cook: as the eldest of thirteen children, she was used to looking after people and she always managed to feed us all – no matter who dropped by, she would find a way of making things stretch. Aunt Lil was a regular visitor; she had been married to my mother's brother Jack, but he had died and she never had any money. Mother wouldn't give her money – she was afraid she would spend it all on alcohol – but she would always feed her. She could conjure up the most wonderful meals: that morning she had been making a stuffing out of sausage meat – the sausage had been purchased under the counter – bulked out with stale bread and chopped swede from the garden; as I left the house to meet Geoff, she was cramming it into the bird's neck.

When I got to the station a train had just arrived, but my brother was nowhere to be seen. The passengers made their way to the gate and I followed the last of them and returned to the waiting room, which was not much warmer than outside. The fire wasn't lit and the ashes of a previous fire blew around in the draughts. I went back outside; it was starting to rain. I stood under the shelter and smoked, tapping the ash onto the tracks.

I had stood on the wooden platform many times before, but only to meet him, never to see him off; I think he would have found it too difficult to leave if any of us had gone with him. It was still early in the afternoon, but the day was so dark and overcast that it may as well have been evening.

I watched the lights of the signal box dissolving into the rain and walked back along the platform; there would be no train for another half an hour at least. Even on the empty platform I felt surrounded by the war: it was there in the official posters and notices, the gaslights which had not been lit since the blackouts. There was no escaping it; it seemed to occupy every waking moment, especially since Geoff had been away. He had completed his training and was now flying on real operations, no longer rehearsals. He hadn't said much in his letters so as not to worry us, but I knew he was in constant danger; the losses at that time in the RAF were appalling: a one in two chance of survival.

I could hear another train approaching and soon thick white smoke engulfed the platform; I couldn't even see my feet. I stared into the windows of the passing carriages trying to make out the faces, and then to my enormous relief I saw Geoff leaning out of one of the windows. I can still see him now: he was wearing his pale blue airman's uniform, his black hair swept across his head. I wondered if his experiences had changed him in some way, but if they had, it didn't show. He seemed his old, happy-go-lucky self; as he stepped down from the train, he poked me playfully in the ribs and ruffled my hair: 'How's our sailor boy? I see the navy are taking all sorts these days.' The only change I could detect was in his eyes: they looked tired and bloodshot, the result, no doubt, of hours of night flying.

I took up his bag and we made towards the gate. By now the rain had stopped, and a fine mist had taken its place, mingling with the railway smoke. We climbed the steps of the wooden bridge, with its steps painted black: 'I thought I'd never see all this again,' he said.

'What's it like up there at night?' I asked him.

'It's exactly like this,' he said pointing at the mist surrounding the bridge. 'When you're flying at night you can't see a thing, but don't worry I think I can get us home alright.' He laughed and again I felt a great sense of relief, that this was one night when we could forget about the war.

When we got home our parents were waiting by the window and they came out to welcome him back. Mother hugged him and he looked over her shoulder and winked at me. 'Are we still on for tonight?' he said. I'd almost forgotten that we were going to the baths; a local band was playing at the dance.

'What about Arthur?' said Geoff – Arthur was our oldest brother. 'I was sorry to miss the wedding.'

'He's alright – still on honeymoon with Dot.'

'Looks like it's just you and me then.'

I carried my brother's things upstairs to the room we shared, and after a few minutes he came up too. I remember he went over to the window and took a long look at the street, perhaps to see what had changed or to hold onto some memory of home for next time he was away. Then he took the saucer which we used as an ashtray from beneath the potted plant on the sill, sat on the bed and lit a cigarette.

'Do you want to catch up on some sleep?'

'No, I'll be alright in a minute. I've been doing a lot of night-flying lately – it really takes it out of you. Sometimes it's a ten hour round trip.'

'What's the new base like?'

'Slap bang in the middle of nowhere. My hut's pretty basic, but we've got a coke stove to keep us warm.'

'Any nice girls up north?'

His face lit up: 'I've been seeing one of the girls on the base, she's in the WAAFs. I got into a spot of bother the other day – I'd asked her out on a date, but I couldn't keep it. We had to land away from base because of bad weather and then we were on ops the next night – she thought I'd stood her up or was with another girl – they take some convincing these Yorkshire girls. You seeing anyone?'

'Not right now.'

'I'll have to get you fixed up tonight. Wait till they hear you're in the navy – you'll be fighting them off,' he laughed.

We washed and went down to dinner and sitting there with Mother and Father and Aunt Lil, Geoff seemed like his old self again; he talked excitedly about his life in the airforce and told us about a Christmas party on the base: 'We were invited to the Officers' Mess and did I get drunk; everything was free – there was a waitress bringing in the drinks on a tray and they never got any further than the door – all the boys just grabbed the glasses and the tray was empty again so off she went to fill it up again; you should have seen us, there were Squadron Leaders, Pilot Officers, and Sergeants all staggering along ...'

'Don't you get drinking too much,' Mother said, 'or you won't be able to fly the plane.'

Soon it was time for us to leave; the clock had just struck seven. Mother kissed us and Father handed us some cigarettes he'd been saving. They stood in the doorway and waved goodbye and we turned and waved back. Geoff looked over our neighbour's car with an appraising eye: it still looked shiny and new – it had stood idle since the petrol restrictions.

'What a beautiful motor,' he said, 'do you think he'd mind if we took it for a spin?' I gave him a doubtful look; I knew he could have started it. 'I'm going to get one of these after the war,' he said, 'just you see if I don't.' The stars were already out. We walked down the hill, past the cemetery where the railings had been taken for the war effort and past the backs of terraces, the windows blacked out. Silent trees and silent streets, everyone was inside. On the opposite corner was a shop that was part of a house – it was called Palmer's and the lady who lived there used to make her own sweets. She must have been nearly eighty, but she had a youthful face; her grey hair was parted down the middle and tied back in a bun. I remember she had a silver hammer to break the toffee, but she couldn't make it anymore because of the sugar rationing: 'Another casualty of war,' Geoff quipped.

Geoff was looking up at the sky as we walked and I knew he was thinking about flying; I followed his gaze and found myself looking up into infinite sky and space. He was quiet now, in contrast to how he'd been during dinner. Then he stopped walking and turned to me:

'We flew over here once,' he said 'at eighteen thousand feet. I must say it looks better from the ground.' He smiled and said: 'You know, sometimes I get scared. I don't want to go back again, but I have to, I suppose I have to.' I felt shaken; I'd never heard him talk like that before, I knew he must have been worried to say something like that. 'Come on,' I said, 'what we need is a drink.'

'Well, if it isn't our Geoff come back to see us,' said the barmaid at the Thimblemill. 'Let me give you a kiss.' She reached out and grabbed his lapel, virtually pulling him across the bar.

We had a whisky at the bar, then Geoff ordered a couple of pints and we found a quiet corner. Geoff took out a pack of cigarettes – he smoked Woodbines like Father. He laid the pack on the table and placed his lighter on top; it had an old coin set into it, which Father had given him. It was one of the good luck charms that he always took with him on ops; most airmen were superstitious and had some talisman of this sort. We sat in silence and smoked, both thinking about the other and what would happen.

3

'Are we still going to the dance?'

'You try and stop me.'

But as we walked up Thimblemill Road, slightly the worse for wear, Geoff was lagging behind; I wondered if he was really alright. I lit a cigarette, lost in my own thoughts – it was a relief when he grabbed me from behind shouting 'Put that light out – unless you want to give the Germans some target practice!' I laughed – that was the Geoff I knew.

Inside the baths, the lady in the ticket booth was scolding some girls for making a mess – they'd been rubbing the sand from the fire-buckets on their legs to give themselves a tan – stockings being in short supply. 'Nice job, too,' said Geoff – just loud enough for the girls to hear – they laughed; and exasperated, the lady frowned at us and waved us through.

I'd never seen the dance so packed as it was that night; couples were queuing, waiting to get on the floor. Most of the men dressed in uniform, cigarettes dangling from their mouths; the girls in the latest fashion: lace dresses which left little to the imagination. Everyone under the spell of the music – it was something you surrendered to, like a drug, like alcohol – it helped you forget all of life's troubles, even the war itself for a little while.

A shout went up as a group of our friends recognized Geoff and two of the girls rushed over and dragged him off to their table. He gave me a look as if to say 'What can I do?', but I didn't mind; I was proud of him and he deserved his moment of glory.

Along one wall, there were lines of chairs where girls were waiting to be asked for a dance, many of them attractive: I noticed Sylvia among them. She smiled at me and I waved, but I didn't feel much like dancing; I was still thinking about what Geoff had said earlier: 'I don't want to go back again.'

The bandleader rapped his baton and asked for requests – as usual, he only asked the best-looking girls. 'You in the red dress,' he said, pointing to a girl at the front. 'What shall we have, then?'

'Chattanooga Choo Choo.'

She turned and gave her friend a smile, and in doing so, I caught her eye for a fraction of a second. That, as they say, was all it took …

I felt drawn to her – this girl who was singing and dancing with her friend – and I clearly wasn't the only one: quite a few men had their eye on her, much to the annoyance of their partners. Her friend, who'd been kicking her legs like a chorus girl, snapped a heel and almost fell, but she caught her by the arm and they both collapsed in a fit of laughter.

There was quite a crowd round them now and for a moment I lost sight of her; I had just found her again when all hell broke loose; the *Chattanooga Choo Choo* was drowned out by the wail of an air raid siren.

It had been a long time since we'd had a raid, but that sound – so distinctive, so unnerving – immediately conjured up the worst days of the Blitz and the crowd dispersed toward the exits – they weren't taking any chances.

I saw she had taken up her coat and was moving towards the exit; for a time, I could see her somewhere in front of me and then she was gone. Now I thought about my brother and my eyes began searching the room for him. As I was nearing the exit, someone tapped me on the shoulder; I spun around and saw Geoff standing there grinning.

'She's a gorgeous piece alright.'

'What are you talking about?'

'That girl you were staring at. Good luck to you, that's all I can say.'

Outside, the siren was still wailing; one girl was covering her ears. Some of the dancers were making their way around the corner, down to the shelter, but others just waited, disinclined to interrupt their evening for what was, in all likelihood, a false alarm. Geoff didn't seem in a hurry either, so I stood there with him and waited.

'Got any cigarettes? – I think I left mine inside.'

'You what? Think how long it took Dad to save those for you!'

I fished out my pack from my breast pocket and he rubbed his hands together in the cold. As he lit the cigarette, he motioned with his head, smiling at me, and I saw that she had not gone down to the shelter; she was standing by the far wall, beneath the poplars which seemed to be covered with a fine film of moisture.

She stood there, poised as if she was about to move, and I felt a sudden urge to get her to stay, I couldn't stand the thought of losing her from my sight.

Without realizing it, I began to walk the short distance towards her; until then I would never have imagined going up to a girl like that – I had always been shy and tongue-tied – but that night I felt a strange kind of assurance, none of the usual trepidation.

When I was no more than two feet away from her, she saw me and gave me a smile, as if she had expected I would come over.

'Do you think it's an air raid?' I said.

'I shouldn't think so, not tonight, but you never can tell.'

I offered her one of my cigarettes. She stood a little away from me and I moved a little closer.

'Did you come here by yourself?' I said.

'No, I came with one of my brothers, but I don't know where he can have got to. Probably still stuck in the pub.'

We talked for a while, about the dances: I mentioned that I hadn't seen her there before and she told me that she'd been going to the dances in town; for a time, she'd been seeing a Belgian airman; he'd had money and had taken her to the Grand Casino, but she hadn't got on with him: 'He kept buying me presents all the time – expensive things. I felt he was trying to buy me, that he wanted me as a possession.' Something struck me about her voice – she hadn't grown up around here, that much was certain, but I couldn't place the accent.

She was shivering slightly in the cold and moved from one foot to the other. We waited and at length the all-clear sounded.

'Well it was nice talking to you,' she said. 'I think I'm going to head off home.'

'Stay for a while,' I said, and my voice betrayed a depth of emotion I myself had been unaware of; it gave her pause and she stayed exactly where she stood. 'Stay for a while, it's still early, we can go for a drink or a dance?'

'I'm not really in the mood for dancing tonight.'

'Stay at least, I've enjoyed talking to you. I'll soon be going off to war myself – I don't know how many more times I'll be able to come here. You wouldn't believe how nice it is just to talk to you.'

4

By now, Geoff was signalling to me that he was going back inside; I nodded to him, as if to say that I'd be along in a minute. But before I could say another word, a young man strode across to us, cutting a line through the groups of people returning inside. Dressed in a uniform I didn't recognize, he was accompanied by a girl with wavy brown hair who followed a couple of paces behind; she seemed a little in awe of him.

'Irene,' he said to the girl I'd been talking to and as soon as he spoke, I could tell he was an American – it was unmistakable. His voice was terse, with a tone of barely suppressed anger: 'We're going now.' He threw me a glance that was like a warning.

'No, I'm staying. There's no need to worry. We've had the all-clear.'

'Don't think for a minute that I'm leaving you here by yourself.'

'I'm not by myself. I'll be perfectly fine.' She spoke calmly and her voice seemed to have a pacifying effect on him; he began to speak more gently.

'It's just that I worry about you.' And turning to me: 'Make sure you get her home alright.'

He took the dark-haired girl by the hand and led her off, but not without glancing back at us.

'Sorry about that,' she said, 'that was my brother and his girlfriend, Charlotte. She's Belgian too, she's the sister of the airman I went out with. He and my brother are in the same squadron together.'

'Shall we go back inside?'

She looked back once more into the cold, gathering darkness that seemed to be welling up between the poplar trees. 'All right,' she said.

We followed the people crowding back into the building, but once inside, the numbers seemed smaller: the floor was empty and things were slow to get going again. The threat of an air raid, harmless though it turned out, had dampened people's spirits.

For a while there was no music – just the shuffling of feet and the clattering of chairs as people began to resettle. It was in this time that I felt most alone with her, as if the surrounding noise had somehow insulated us from the rest of the world. Now that she was there across the table, I marvelled again at her beauty – I couldn't take my eyes off her.

'There's something I wanted to ask you,' I said, finally having gathered my thoughts, 'your brother's American?'

'Yes, he's in the American airforce. I was born there too.'

'His accent's a lot stronger than yours,' I said.

'Yes, I was only eight when we came back – he's older than me.'

'Came back?'

'Do you want the long version or the short?'

I wanted the ten-volume version, but just smiled.

'Well, my parents came from round here – and my eldest brother was born here as well. But Dad's brother was doing really well in the States and they decided to sell up and join him. Mom always said it was meant to be. You're not going to believe this.'

'Give me a try.'

'You see Mom was originally engaged to this other man. But one day she went to a Fortune Teller. The woman told her "You'll cross water," but my mother had no money and she didn't know anyone abroad, so she shook her head, but the woman insisted: "You'll cross it more than once," she said. "And there's a man in uniform here, and you're going to marry him." Well my mother's fiancé was a civilian – and she said "I don't think so, you must be mistaken," but the woman looked straight past her and said "That's what will happen. I can't tell you anymore." She left and didn't think anything of it.

'My mother used to perform in the music halls at the time and she needed a good picture for front of house. She'd been to the photographer's – the one in the Great Western Arcade. She was very attractive and the man had offered to take her pictures for free if he could display one in the window. It was a beautiful picture: she looked like a film star, leaning back with her hands behind her neck. Anyway, when she went back to the shop, the photographer was talking to a young man and they stopped talking and stared at her. The man was wearing regimentals and sitting in front of a backdrop waiting to have his picture taken.'

'And that was your father?'

'Yes. They started talking and he told her that he'd seen her photo in the window and had been asking the photographer about her when she came

in. They immediately liked each other and agreed to see each other again.'
She smiled at this, before continuing:

'They were married shortly after that and then my brother Bill was born – they named him after Dad's brother Bill, the one in America. Have you heard of the Great Lakes? Lake Michigan?'

'Yes, we had to learn them all for a geography test.'

She laughed: 'That was where he lived. He wrote saying how much better things were over there, how much work there was. My father didn't have enough money for the whole family to go, so they did it in stages: he went out first and worked there for a year, then he sent the boat-fare for my mother to join him. When Dad brought her to the new house, it was all furnished and there was even a piano in the lounge – something she'd always wanted. Uncle Bill told us that Dad had worked at two jobs to save up the money.

'There was a lake behind the house – more like a sea than a lake – and in the summer, we used to swim out to a raft and look back at the shore; there were huge trees all along the shoreline. And we were always diving off rocks and things; my brothers would put me up on their shoulders, like a troupe of acrobats in a circus, and we'd dive in. That was the happiest time in my life ...'

'What made you all come back?' I said.

'We had to – my father died ... he got meningitis. They rushed him to hospital and said he only had a few days. He'd been injured in the First War at Salonica – he'd been in an explosion which damaged his ears – and the doctor said that could have started it. He must have wanted to live – he lasted another five weeks ... I can still remember the funeral: his coffin was across the room in the corner and there was some kind of large house plant next to it. There were a lot of people in the house and I remember someone lifting me up to look at him. He looked like he was asleep. They told me I should kiss him – "Kiss the dead and they'll leave you alone." I could still feel the cold on my lips a long time after ...' Her voice faltered and almost came to a stop: 'I don't know why I'm telling you all this. You must think I'm mad.'

'It's the war – it makes it easier to talk about things, somehow. Right now, I feel I could tell you anything.'

'My Dad was only thirty-seven when he died. The next thing I remember was Mom saying that we were all going back to England and so the prediction came true: she crossed the sea twice. It was something she regretted later – we'd have been better off staying in America. My uncle begged her to stay out there and a friend of my father's who'd lost his wife offered to help with the house and the garden. And they used to give you sacks of flour and coal in America – they looked after you that way. It was Mom's family in England who persuaded her to go back, but they never considered that she would be dependent on them – a woman coming back with four children, they don't want you living with them.'

'They wanted to see her, but they didn't want the responsibility.'

'Yes, that's it – exactly that. As soon as we got off the boat, she knew it was a mistake; she said it was as if something or someone told her "Get back on the boat and go back." The voyage had been terrible; I'd been sick all the way back, and I remember running along the deck, and these funnels would bring up the smell from the kitchens and make me sick. And when we got there, the family didn't want to know; we lived with our grandparents for about a week, until Mom got a job, but on her first day of work they said "Where do you think you're going? You're not leaving those kids here."'

I reached out and touched her hand and she let it rest there for a moment.

'Well, that's how I got my American accent. It's late – I should go.'

'Let me walk back with you.'

'I'll be fine, really.'

'No, I insist, I want to.'

She took her coat. The floor was now full of dancers again, but the atmosphere seemed to jar with the story she'd told me; I couldn't think of anything else.

We made our way to the exit, circling round the dancers. I kept thinking 'I haven't spent any time with Geoff' – that was the whole point of going out that evening and it pricked at my conscience – I hadn't even said goodbye.

'Just give me a minute,' I said to her. 'I need to find my brother, we were coming out tonight to celebrate his leave.' I saw him at last coming into the entrance hall; he had evidently been to the pub again. He stumbled slightly then straightened himself up when he saw Irene.

'This is my brother. Geoff, this is Irene.' She held out her hand to him; he gave her a winning smile – I could tell that he liked her.

'Your brother's kindly offered to take me home, but we can stay with you if you like.'

'No, I'll be alright, I've got a couple of mates I want to catch up with.' He grabbed my arm, gave it a squeeze, and whispered: 'Don't keep the lady waiting.'

Then, as we passed him to go out, he gave me a strange look. I often wondered later whether he had some premonition of what was to come; whether he envied me the life he thought I would have. Perhaps he knew, as many airmen did, that his life would be cut short.

Part II:

August 1969 – March 1970

1

Earlier that day, my daughter, Sarah, had been to get her exam results: Irene and I had gone with her to Holly Lodge Grammar School, where she'd been a pupil. When we reached the gates, Sarah had said: 'Can you wait here for me?'

'Don't be silly, we want to find out as much as you do.' Irene had sounded slightly hurt.

'What if I've done badly? No, I'd rather go myself.'

We watched her make her way down the drive; there was something hesitant about her steps that made me feel protective towards her and I moved as if to go after her, but Irene, having suddenly taken our daughter's side, said: 'No, let her go by herself if that's what she wants.'

I felt awkward standing there waiting and I'm sure she did too. I wondered whether she'd stay with me now that Sarah – it was almost certain – was off to university. She'd been the last main tie between us and now she was going away …

'Oh no,' said Irene, 'look at her.' Sarah, eyes downcast, was coming back up the drive, while around her, you could hear the carefree laughter of girls finished with school.

'Never mind,' said Irene, 'you can stay here with us, now.'

'No, I got in – two A's and a B.'

'That's wonderful. Why the long face?'

'I was just thinking about Grandma – how's she going to cope when I'm not around?'

My mother, Mary, was now a widow, my father having died some years before. Since then, Sarah had been a great comfort to her grandmother – she used to go round a couple of nights a week after school and Mary would spoil her. I'd tried to see my mother when I could, but it was difficult with work – or at least that's what I told myself. But there was another reason I didn't visit her that often in later years: too many memories of Geoff in that house.

That evening, we'd gone round so Sarah could tell her the results: my mother already had a card for her, with money inside. She wasn't leaving us for a few more weeks, not until early October, but we already knew we were going to miss her dreadfully. My mother had wanted to look through some of Sarah's baby photos: there was one in particular – it had been the old man's favourite – taken when she was about four years old. It had been hand-tinted in blues and purples and she had been wearing a chiffon scarf.

She had sent me upstairs to look for it: 'I think it's in a suitcase with some of your father's old stuff, on top of the wardrobe in Geoff's room.'

Even after twenty-five years, we still thought of it as his. My daughter used it when she stayed over – there were clean sheets, starched pillow cases, but despite this, the room felt cold, a room that was no longer used.

I pulled over the chair – there were two of Sarah's books – German poetry: Heine and Rilke. 'How times change,' I thought – we'd been at war twenty-five years ago – if someone had told me back then that my daughter would be studying German, I wouldn't have believed it. I placed the books on the bed and standing on the chair, reached over the decorative rail on top of the wardrobe, but where you'd have expected the 'top' to be, there was a sunken level – a hidden recess of about eight or nine inches; as I moved the case, I could feel something else underneath. Then I remembered what it was: the dark green box containing Geoff's personal effects. It had lain there forgotten.

The old man had made it for him before he left for flight training; the last time I'd seen it was after he was killed, when it was returned to us, but I hadn't looked through it then – it had been too painful.

Standing on tiptoe, I got hold of the lid, but the box was heavier than I thought and the weight caused it to open suddenly: the contents fell to the floor, and for a moment, the air swirled with dust and flakes of paint.

'Are you alright up there?' I heard my mother call.

'Yes, I'll be down in a minute.'

I knelt down to pick up his things: an airman's pocket bible and prayer book, his sergeant's stripes. His black fountain pen – the one he'd used to write his letters home: I unscrewed the top and scribbled on the back of a receipt – the ink had long since dried. There was a rust-coloured notebook filled with his handwriting: complex sums and calculations to do with fuel consumption, headwinds and tailwinds. On one page, he'd pasted a newspaper cutting about a Lancaster bomber that had managed to pull out of a 16,000 foot dive.

I turned a few pages and found a list of targets: Berlin, Essen – the last – Amiens – was missing. By the time he was killed he'd flown twenty-five missions, just five short of the thirty required.

'Only five more,' I thought: 'five more and you'd still be here.'

I hadn't expected to find any sweetheart photos; there was an unwritten rule that if you were killed, your mates usually cleared out anything of that sort so as not to add further distress to a wife or girlfriend back home.

But as I was leafing through the exercise book, a photo slipped out from between the pages and landed face down on the floor. I looked at it for a moment and hesitated to pick it up – I knew already what it was, or rather who. His words came floating back: in one letter, he'd asked for some photos taken at his twentieth birthday: *Can you send me one of my future sister-in-law as well?*

I picked it up: Irene, as I knew it would be. It must have been taken in April '44: her hair was darker in this one – when I met her at the dance, she had highlights, but this was her natural colour. 'Your mates missed this one,' I thought, almost laughing, but not quite. They might have taken out all the others, the WAAFs who used to wave him off, the girl from Pontefract, but not this one. But then maybe I was wrong, perhaps for him too, there weren't any other girls – only Irene.

2

I did a number of jobs after the war: I worked as a delivery man, delivering milk and bread; those were still the days of horses and carts and I had a wonderful black horse. I was the only one who could handle him, he used to thrash about in the stable and everyone else at the depot was scared of him; they'd say: 'Don't go near him, he's in a nasty mood.' But I would talk to him, I think it used to soothe him, and he would usually quieten down after a while and then I could slip the bridle over him. Once we were out on the streets, he was as good as gold; sometimes a car would come too close for comfort, that used to unnerve him, but there weren't many cars in those days. I used to love driving the cart, especially in the summer months, it felt like the best job in the world. You sat high up, though sometimes you had to duck the low branches. And then one day, they stopped using the horses, we were told that they were being replaced by vans. I knew they would probably slaughter the old horses; I didn't want to stay after that.

For a while, I was holding down two jobs: I was doing the deliveries in the mornings and working in a petrol station at night. But that was around the time that I discovered I had TB and had to go to the sanatorium. Irene worked in a shoe shop and my parents helped us out with money.

When I came out of the sanatorium, I was unable to work for a long time; they sent you home in those days, but you were still convalescing – it was like a continuation of the regime: bed rest, light exercise if you were up to it, but there were days when I was too weak physically to do anything. I tried to get jobs, but they didn't really want to take me: probably the fear of TB. When they asked what I'd been doing for three years and I told them I'd been in the sanatorium, you could see what they were thinking: *he'll always be ill and weak, maybe even contagious* – you didn't stand a chance.

For a few years, I was in and out of work … then in 1964, I got the job I have now – as caretaker of a school. The pay wasn't great, but it came with a house – that was all taken care of – so I landed on my feet. I wasn't as good with my hands as Dad or Geoff, but I had learned enough by watching and spending time with them that I could manage. Gradually, I learned, I read up on the heating system and electrics … until I found I could carry out most of the repairs myself.

It was strange at first, being 'back at school' – it made me think about my own schooldays. I'd always been good at maths – working out sums in my head – and one of the teachers had encouraged me to take the entrance exam for university. I was still deciding when the war intervened and the decision was made for me.

That was why I was so pleased when Sarah was accepted, though I worried a little about the types she would meet there. In her last year at school, she'd been to see what they called 'a happening' – some modern dance group from Germany. I'd dropped her and a friend at the Arts Centre, and when I went back to pick them up, there were police cars outside, sirens blazing. My first thought was that there'd been a fire or some kind of accident – I was beside myself – but it turned out one of the performers had locked the door from the inside – 'to stop the audience leaving,' Sarah told me later. In the end, they'd had to smash it down.

When they finally got out, half of audience were smeared in what looked like blood – it was awful. 'That's the last time you go anywhere like that,' I said when I had them safely back in the car – 'What on earth happened?'

Both girls laughed nervously, but it was Sarah who spoke up: 'We went in and sat down and then the dancers came on – they weren't wearing anything on their feet. And the men got out these giant tins of red paint – they started throwing them at the backdrop and around the stage and walking in it. Then …' – the friend, Valerie, shrieked with laughter – 'then,' Sarah continued, 'the men started taking their clothes off and the women were *painting them*. And then the women stripped and got up on the men's shoulders.'

At that point, some members of audience had tried to leave, but the dancers, having anticipated this, had already locked the exits. I wasn't happy about it – and told her as much – but was relieved she was ok.

On the way home, the girls tried to make sense of what they'd just seen: Valerie thought it was about the war – 'the slaughter of civilians' – hence the red paint. 'But they went a bit far, don't you think?'

'Better than real blood, I suppose,' Sarah had said.

I was still angry and said nothing, but when I thought about it later, I realized she was right.

3

It was difficult to believe that Sarah was now the same age as I was when I went to war – the time had gone so quickly and I'd seen so little of her, particularly during the early years: I'd missed her first steps, her first words – all of those things. That was the time I was in and out of hospital, and then I was shut away for three years in the sanatorium.

It might as well have been a cell door slamming shut; they didn't let children in to visit you – it really affected our relationship later on. I hardly saw her – only when Irene and my mother or father visited together so one of them could look after her. While Irene was visiting me, my father would walk through the grounds with my little girl so I could catch a glimpse of her through the French windows. He would lift her onto the balustrade and get her to wave at me, but she had no idea who she was waving to – I was just the stranger at the window.

When I came home, she didn't know who I was – I think she was a little bit scared of me – understandably so. I must have looked pretty ghastly after all the operations and the treatments – I think she saw the scarring once when I was changing my shirt. If I was in the room with her and my father, she'd always run to her grandpa.

That made me jealous at first – to see how close they were – but not for long. It was the best thing that could have happened for the old man; I think he'd transferred all his love for Geoffrey to Sarah.

But our relationship remained distant – it took a long time for the ice to thaw. I blame myself for that – I'd become very quiet and withdrawn in the sanatorium; you were isolated, your only concern was getting over your illness. Within those walls, you were completely cut off from the outside world.

But then, you go back into society – I couldn't cross the road, or take a bus, I was too scared. I found it very difficult to cope: crowds of people would make me feel anxious. I think it was the way people looked at you; you felt stigmatized by the disease. Not by everyone, never by Irene or my parents, but you saw who your friends were; some friends would visit you a couple of times, but you could see the fear on their faces when you coughed and then their visits would tail off. I can't say that I blamed them – it was a terrible disease and you wouldn't want to catch it for the world. But you get influenced by their fears; you feel that you're going to pass on some germ or infection, even when you've been given the all-clear.

And that made it difficult to get close to her – I suppose I was always trying to keep my distance to protect her, it made it difficult for any sort of relationship to develop between us. I was so used to people's scared reactions that that's how you begin to think of yourself, that you're contagious.

We only became close when she was older, in her teens, and that was because of Irene; she had met someone else, and I think we both felt abandoned. Sarah used to get really bad nosebleeds – she had a weak vein in her nose and they were difficult to stop – usually she would have to go to hospital to get it cauterized. But one day I came home from work and found her with a neighbour; she'd had a bad nosebleed, and the neighbour had wrapped her in a blanket. The woman was shaking her head and I knew instantly what had happened – Irene had left her on her own. When the neighbour had gone, I asked her, as if reading her thoughts:

'You know where she's gone, don't you?'

'Yes, I do. She shouldn't have left me, should she?'

I hadn't felt angry with Irene ever until that moment, but I felt angry with myself as well. I realized I would have to go with her in the ambulance – the thought of going to a hospital, *any* hospital, after being in the sanatorium terrified me. I could feel myself breaking into a cold sweat and I tried to breathe quietly so I wouldn't distress Sarah more.

I can see it all rationally now, but at the time, my memories of the sanatorium were still raw. They used to blindfold you and put a camera down your throat, no anaesthetic, and you'd gag – you'd almost choke. It had left me with a dread of hospitals.

I put my arms around her and said 'Don't worry, it'll stop soon.'

'I never knew you knew,' she said, 'I thought you might, but I was afraid to tell you.'

'How did you find out?' I asked.

'He gave me and Mom a lift in his car and …' she went on reluctantly, 'they gave me some money to get sweets, but they dropped me quite a way from the shop and I had to walk – and I thought "Why have they dropped me here?" I looked back and I saw them … they were kissing.'

I could tell that she felt equally betrayed.

'She won't change,' I said, shaking my head.

She turned to me: 'Why don't you leave her then?'

'I love her. I'll never leave your mother or you.'

4

There had been an evening concert at the school; when I finally got back, Irene had gone to bed. I turned down the heating and went to make some tea in the kitchen, closing the door so as not to make a noise. Then I went into the living room, put on the side-lamp and sat in the armchair by the window. For a while I watched television with the sound down, watching the flickering images light up the room. I got tired and switched it off. As I sat there, my eye was drawn to the framed photo of Sarah which took pride of place on the mantelpiece. The photo had appeared in the local newspaper and they'd sent us a copy: in her final year at school, she'd played Lady Macbeth in the end of year production – everyone had said how marvellous she was. In the photo, she was coming down the stairs, wearing a white night-dress and holding a lamp in the sleepwalking scene.

She was now at university up in Hull, studying German and Drama – it was one of three universities to offer the choices she wanted. But I think it was more than that – I think she wanted to get away from home.

I'd missed her; she'd been back, of course, to visit, but not as often as I would have liked. She didn't have much money and I didn't have much to give her – she had stayed in halls for the first year, sharing a room with her friend Jacmel, but in the second year she'd moved out to save money. She was living on the main road into Hull, in a grotty little back-to-back house. I'd been up there to help her move in and clean up the place – the hot tap didn't work and there had been slugs on the carpet.

I was proud of Sarah – she was the first in our family to go to university, but I wished she had stayed closer to home so I could help her out more. The last time I'd seen her was in the half-term; I'd driven up and taken her to a café where you could get fish and chips served with bread and butter and steaming hot tea.

I'd told myself that I was going to see my daughter – and I was – but there was another reason as well, a curiosity to see the places my brother had stayed in the war, which had grown stronger with each passing year. It was the first time I had been up to Yorkshire – 'Bomber Country' as it was known in the war; on the way back, I'd been to Betty's Bar in York and looked at the signatures on the mirror behind the bar, the names of airmen in the war who had scratched their signature with a diamond pen – I wondered how many, like Geoffrey, hadn't returned. I'd always had the feeling that he might have signed it as well – he mentioned nights out in York in his letters – but try as I might, I couldn't find his signature – the barmaid told us later that some of the mirrors had been destroyed in the war during an air raid.

And I went to see Geoff's base – what remained of the old airfield. I left the car in the nearby village and walked around the perimeter track; the sun was setting – it must have looked similar on the day he went off to bomb the railway yards in Amiens, and I saw what he would have seen, now twenty-five years on. The concrete shell of the control tower, the Nissen huts converted to farm buildings, a rusting water tower. Dusk was falling now. If you squinted, you could imagine what it would have been like, you could almost see the convoys of vans and lorries taking the crews out to their planes, you could almost hear the roar of the engines. Staring down the runway, you could imagine wave after wave of Halifax bombers filling the evening sky like a dark cloud. I closed my eyes, but when I opened them again, the illusion vanished: time had moved on, the airfield was being reclaimed as farmland, the runways slowly disappearing beneath the grass.

5

All that was left now were his letters and his RAF portrait – that portrait which had stood on my parents' mantelpiece until the day my mother died. I'd been with him on the day it was taken: I could still remember how we'd walked down to the photographer's on Smethwick High Street. Geoff had just finished his training at the OTU and so was finally able to wear the coveted blue RAF uniform and stripes. He'd grown up a lot in the time he'd been away: still not yet twenty, his demeanour and mannerisms were those of someone much older, his eyes sharper as if he could see beyond what other people saw.

'You've no idea,' he said, 'when you join up, it's like joining an elite group. The pilots and navigators, well they're in a different league from us engineers, but I got to learn how to fly the plane too.' He laughed: 'They couldn't build a plane though. After a month in that factory, I reckon I could!'

Being in the RAF had given him an air of confidence, a kind of aura that wasn't lost on women; the barmaids at the Blue Gates were both giving him the eye ...

Looking at that photograph now, twenty-five years later, you could still feel that aura. In the portrait, he was standing half in profile, smiling to himself, almost breaking into a laugh. It was quite unlike the serious military portraits of grave, grim-faced men that you often see – it had captured his sense of humour – but at the same time, you were aware of something deeper, beyond that.

His portrait had stood on the mantelpiece for all those years, and yet we rarely talked about him – it only reminded us of what we'd lost. My mother would always cry on his birthdays and at Christmas – that was the worst time, when we were all sat around the table; she would make an excuse that she'd left something on the stove, but we all knew why she'd gone out – we felt the same. My daughter must have picked up on that; she was very perceptive even as a child. She'd grown up with that silence and in some way had become party to it. But I knew that one day she would ask me about Geoffrey.

It was after my mother had died – Sarah had come home for the funeral. My mother had been terribly lonely ever since my father died. It had been sudden and totally unexpected – he was undergoing a minor operation. It was close to Bonfire Night and he'd prepared his usual massive bonfire and Guy Fawkes. He'd told my daughter he'd be home to let off the rockets and had died a happy man.

Her sisters had also died. I tried to see her when I could, but it was difficult with work; we needed the money and I was often ill and had to sleep whenever I could just to get myself to work. It had been better when Sarah was in the sixth form – my mother's house was closer to her school and she used to go round and sleep over – she said it was quieter there and she could get her work done. And I think my mother missed having someone to look after and to cook for. It was in the middle of the night that she died – I wasn't there, she died alone.

Together, Sarah and I had gone round to begin the sad task of clearing the house – I'd asked her to come with me to see what she wanted to keep. It was the same house that Geoff and I had grown up in and each room contained memories. I walked around to take a last look: in the room we'd shared, I could still see the cigarette burns on the mattress that he'd tried to hide from Mother all those years before.

I had boxed up the photo albums and letters and put Geoff's portrait on top. But the frame was too large and I couldn't close it. Sarah left off the crate she was packing and came over and picked it up; she was silent for a while and I wondered what she was thinking.

Finally she said: 'I always knew something terrible had happened to him, even as a child.'

'How did you know?'

'It was the way you all looked at it – that portrait. It used to scare me to look at it – it was the thought of how he died, and not knowing – that was what scared me. Grandpa used to say "It's all in the past, darling. Don't worry yourself."' She placed it back on top of the box, her eyes still fixed on it. 'Why did you never talk to me about him?'

'It was too painful.'

'It was Aunt Hazel who told me in the end … about the telegram, how he was reported missing at first …'

'Yes, it was weeks before we knew for certain.'

I felt myself starting to shake – I hadn't talked to anyone about Geoff for a long time. I fumbled in my jacket for cigarettes and lit one, but it made me splutter; I would have to give them up before they gave me up.

'Are you alright, Dad?'

'Yes, I'm alright,' I said, aware of how unconvincing I sounded. 'I didn't know you'd talked to Aunt Hazel.' Hazel was Aunt Lil's daughter, but she had only been a child when Geoffrey was killed – her mother must have told her about him. 'What else did she say?'

'She told me about the time when Arthur broke your foot and Geoff made him pay for it.'

Even as she spoke, I was back there running down the passage and screaming for Mother. As I struggled with the gate, he smashed the brick down on my foot. Tears welled in my eyes, as much from my brother's needless cruelty as the pain and I blurted out, 'You've broke my foot you bugger!', but he just stood there laughing – Arthur was a terrible bully. I hobbled back into the house and Mother gave him a hiding, but his real come-uppance came later:

'When Geoff found out, he battered him and blacked one of his eyes – he never bothered me after that.'

She laughed. 'What was he like when you were growing up?'

'He always looked out for me, being a year older – I looked up to him. We often went to Bridgnorth at the weekend, fishing, we used to take the bikes. Arthur was a lazybones, he'd never get up on time, so usually it would just be Geoff and me. We'd cycle to Dudley, past the old monastery and then on to Bridgnorth. It was all country back then, farms and thatched cottages, even scarecrows out in the fields. We'd go to the old tackle shop – it was always our dream to catch a pike – there was a huge stuffed pike – a river monster – behind the counter encased in glass, its mouth upturned in a dreadful leer. We never caught our elusive pike, but there were other fish, chub and dace, and Geoff always seemed to know the best spots. We'd walk down the banks, eyeing the currents, looking for where it quickened; he'd point out the best spots, the glides where the water became more rapid. We'd seen old men use the berries that hung down from the trees over the river for bait. He used to say: "If you see the line twitch, reel him in quick. If you leave him, he'll take the line down into the sunken roots and that'll be the end of it, you'll never see it again.'" Strange how years later, I could still see that long-dead summer, the quality of the light, I could smell it, I could hear the river rushing. The shade of the trees, the dark spots on the river.

'Once we caught – well Geoff caught – it must have been a three or four-pounder at least. He steered it, I netted it.'

'You were close to him, weren't you?'

'Yes, I was always close to Geoffrey – and Arthur turned out alright in the end.'

'How did you hear about his death?'

'I was at sea when it happened – we didn't know the details till much later. But your Mom told me something that always stayed with me … She'd thrown a birthday party for Geoff – she and Rita – they'd organised it in the room above the Blue Gates. And he'd been drinking quite a lot and suddenly he'd disappeared from the party.'

'What happened?'

'They went out to look for him and they found him on the stairs crying …'

And I began to tell her everything.

Part III:

March – June 1944

1

As usual, I'd gone to meet her after she finished work at the cake factory on Windmill Lane, and we'd gone straight from there to the cinema – an early evening showing at the Prince's on Smethwick High Street. I can't remember now what film we saw – something with Bette Davis? I didn't really watch the films, I just watched Irene.

As we came out, a group of soldiers were shoving, jostling their way in, raucously drunk: as we squeezed past, there were shouts of 'What yer doing with him, love?' and 'I can show you a better time than he can.' I think I was invisible to them without a uniform – they only gave you a lapel badge in the Merchant Navy which most of us saw as an insult and refused point blank to wear. A uniform would at least have put me on the same footing: wasn't the job I was about to do as dangerous as theirs?

Irene must have noticed my reddening face, my clenched fists: 'Don't take it so seriously,' she said, 'they're just drunk.' But it still bothered me, it bothered me a lot.

It was now quite certain that I would be departing for the war: the training had been quite rigorous and I'd had to undergo another medical after a bad bout of bronchitis, but had been passed fit for service. My name had been added to the Merchant Navy pool and it was only a matter of time.

In the meantime, I saw Irene almost every day. She lived at her stepfather's house, with her mother and younger brother, Alfred; the older two, Bill and Bob, had left home by then. Her mother, Polly, was kind, and in her blue eyes I could see the attractive woman she must have been when her portrait hung in the photographer's window years before, but life had treated her badly; she had the look of someone who had struggled to survive.

Her stepfather was a difficult person to talk to – Irene had no time for him and I think that affected how I saw him. He worked on the railways and when he came home he would go straight to the table and sit and wait for his evening meal to be brought to him, without saying a word. I wondered whether he resented his stepchildren living there with him – Irene never said, but that was the feeling I got. He would watch them with apparent contempt, and any conversation was strained, to say the least. You could hear the clock ticking in the hallway. Sometimes he smoked a pipe and it was then that I noticed his hands as he struggled to fill it with tobacco; he'd been in the last war and some of his fingers were missing as the result of an explosion.

I finally received my orders in March '44, not yet knowing the name of the ship, only the port I was sailing from. I was to take the train to Liverpool and stay overnight, ready to leave sometime the following day. In the event, I left home a day early. Like Geoff, I'd persuaded my parents not to come with me to the station; it would be better that way, I said, there would be crowds at the station and I didn't want to say goodbye like that, in all that noise and confusion. That was partly the truth.

And so it was on a quiet morning that I walked to the bottom of Mansion Crescent. As I turned to wave, I saw my mother clutch my father's hands and the old man put a comforting arm around her. Even though I'd thought about it before, it didn't really sink in until that moment – that I might not see them again.

The walk to the station seemed like something happening in a dream, or to someone else; I couldn't really believe that any of it was taking place, that I was leaving my mother and father, perhaps for the last time, while the world that morning appeared so outwardly unchanged: the old four-sided clock that hung above the platform, its faces yellowed behind misted glass; the soot-blackened brick wall that screened the track from the back gardens of houses. Aside from government posters, the station was hardly any different than before the war; the train I was waiting to catch was the same train I'd caught at least a hundred times.

I opened my wallet; inside was the travel voucher they had sent me – pre-stamped for Liverpool – but instead, I counted out my change and bought a ticket to Birmingham.

When the train arrived at New Street, I made my way to the exit barrier and went out into the city.

I'd thought of that day for the past week or so, of what I would do when it came, so it seemed strange finally to be acting it out. It crossed my mind that no one knew where I was and that for the next few hours at least, I was truly free.

First, I went to the bank. I checked the balance in my pass-book – I knew already what the figure would be, but was still dismayed to see it in writing: all the dance halls and films I'd taken her to had made quite a dent in my savings. If I took out the rest, I wouldn't be able to eat for the next two days, not until I was onboard my ship – what if it was delayed? The Merchant Navy hadn't advanced me any pay. A queue was now forming behind me and the female cashier was shaking her head – I quickly filled out a cheque for the entire amount and cashed it.

It was good to get outside again, in the fresh air. I walked around for a while, lugging the heavy suitcase, but the time passed slowly, so I decided to find somewhere to sit down. I bought some cigarettes from a tobacconist and went on until I came to the cathedral square. It was a mild day – a foretaste of summer. I sat down on one of the benches, and smoked and watched the other people in the square. Sitting on the opposite row was a woman in a black schoolmistress-type outfit, with a pram of the same colour parked at her side. Her clothes made her seem older than she was; at a second glance, you could see she was pretty in fact, and I spent some time trying to determine from her appearance whether she was the child's mother or some paid nanny. An old man emerged from the back of one of the buildings with his dog – a huge Alsatian with a dusty coat and it walked very close to the chap, looking up at him. By the look of the man, it was the dog that got most of the rations. As they passed, the dog lunged towards me and I rubbed his head; the old fellow smiled and said: 'Don't ever get old, mate.'

It rained later, and as I walked down Corporation Street, into Stephenson Place, people were putting up black umbrellas. I took shelter under the covered arches of the Queens Hotel, which was also the old entrance to New Street Station. I finally put down the suitcase – an elderly porter almost grabbed it out of my hand: 'Are you staying with us, sir?' 'Yes, I am.' He looked as frail and undernourished as the old chap I'd seen with the dog – all the young men had been called up while those my father's age were either in the Home Guard or doing essential work. He was about to take the case from me when Irene walked out of the station – she'd arrived earlier than I expected.

She smiled when she saw me, but her expression changed when she noticed the suitcase:

'Have they changed the time of your departure?'

'No. I'm still leaving tomorrow. Nothing's changed.'

'What did you bring your case for? … I thought we were going to that dance.'

'We still can, if you want to. Or –'

'– *we could get a room in this hotel*. Is that what you were going to say?'

'It might have crossed my mind.'

'Can you afford it?'

'I drew out my life's savings this morning.'

She laughed. 'I think I want to go to the dance,' she said, but she caught my hand and I felt like the luckiest man alive.

We went into the reception – it was just as magnificent on the inside and made quite an impression. I felt rather self-conscious as I signed the register – I had never stayed in a hotel before – but we were just two of the many guests and the desk clerk paid us no special attention. He reeled off a list of restrictions – 'baths not to exceed five inches of water … blackout curtains to be checked at 8pm' – then we were allowed to go through for dinner.

'What shall we have?' said Irene.

I studied the menu carefully, aware that this could be my last meal for two days.

Irene looked so happy – and beautiful. Some of the men in the restaurant gazed across at her, but she was oblivious to them, laughing and telling me about her friend's efforts to steal someone's boyfriend, which had gone disastrously wrong.

Over dessert, the subject of Geoff's birthday came up – he was trying to get home for it; it was unlikely I would be back in time. We were eating bread and butter pudding: 'Quite good, but not as good as your Mom's,' Irene said. 'I'll have to try and get some more sugar so she can make one for Geoff's party.'

'Party?' I said.

'Yes, I want to do something special – make it the best party ever. I'll get your Dad to make some beer for the men -'

'- Men? Who are you thinking of inviting?'

Coffee was served and the guests began to retire for the evening. I glanced across at Irene, wondering if she was feeling as nervous as I was about later on – we hadn't slept together yet – but if she was, she didn't show it.

Feeling in need of some Dutch courage, I asked a waiter if I could get a whisky, only to be told they were out. Gin? Same reply. I could have kicked myself – I should have known better than to wait till the end of the meal – didn't I know there was a war on?

The waiter apologised, mumbling he would see what he could do. But Irene shook her head – 'We're fine, thanks' – and when he'd left us, she said:

'You don't need it, really you don't.' And I knew everything would be alright.

Later that night, I was woken by the noise of a train passing, uncomfortably close: the light fittings shook and the windows rattled – it sounded like it was going to come through the wall. I watched Irene stir and then turn and go back to sleep. Her words came back to me: 'I want to do something special – make it the best party ever.' I should have been grateful, I knew, but my mind kept replaying the words, twisting their meaning. I was no stranger to jealousy: I'd seen the looks men gave her, I'd had to stand aside and watch while they danced with her; this was the inevitable downside of having such an attractive girl. But jealousy towards other men was one thing – I'd never been jealous of my brother and didn't want to start now.

I told myself I was being ridiculous – I could count on one hand the number of times she'd met Geoff. And yet ... was there something I'd missed? I thought about the last time he'd been home on leave – the night Irene had come round to my parents'. I sensed that she liked him. And Geoff? Geoff, who was normally expansive and at ease in any company, would speak more carefully when she was around, as if he was considering each word, while Irene would often glance across at him and smile; he would look away, as if he hadn't seen.

You got used to not seeing light coming through curtains – it was part of the war, but like a blind person, your other senses become more acute, you relied on your hearing to tell you when it was morning – the creaking of floorboards, footsteps in the corridors. And after a lull, the early morning trains began to depart ...

Irene came with me to the platform – we had to cross over the footbridge under the great glass roof which had been blacked out with tar at the start of the war. Not the best place for goodbyes.

'I wish I was coming with you,' she said.

'I wish you were too, but not this place, not now.'

'Why don't we get another train, run away from all this?'

'Listen, when I get back, we'll go somewhere good. I'll even take you to the sea, and you know I can't swim.'

The guard was closing all the doors and as she held me, I wondered if I'd ever see her again.

As the train pulled away, I felt I was being overtaken by a fate over which I had no control, a war in which I wanted no part. As far as I saw it, the world was taking me away from the only things I cared about – Irene and my family. I couldn't escape that fate – the fate of so many others, my brother included.

When the train got in to Liverpool, I took out the directions I'd been sent and headed out into the city. The letter was somewhat vague in its details, perhaps for fear it should fall into the wrong hands. On the stairs of a subway, I asked a woman for directions, but she said she was also new to the town and didn't know. Finally, after circling for a while, I caught sight of a street name from the letter, and found my way from there. The address I'd been given turned out to be a lodging-house that had been requisitioned by the navy. A three-storey Victorian building that must have been attractive in its day, dark green paint was flaking from the eaves and from the windows of a damp-looking basement. I went in and found myself in a poorly lit vestibule decorated in a heavy dark wallpaper. In the corner, beside the reception desk, there was a large house plant and on the wall behind, a wood-and-glass casing containing the pull wires of an old bell system. An elderly woman with dyed red hair came in and stood behind the desk.

'First time?' she said.

I hesitated, unsure what she meant.

'From home,' she added.

'Yes.'

'I can usually tell. Those who have been to war and those who are on the way. Besides, they send me lists of recruits for each day – you're the last to arrive, I think.'

I wondered why she had asked me when she already knew the answer, but I suppose she was simply making conversation. She could only speak in generalities. She would never get to know any of those who stayed in her house; they would be here one or two days at most before a ship came up. I handed over the documentation I'd brought and she compared it against the list on her desk. Then I followed her up the stairs to an attic room with a low sloping ceiling. 'Remember, the front door is bolted at ten,' she said as she turned to go. I hadn't planned on going out, or even considered the possibility of doing so until her mention of a curfew; however, it was still early, so after unpacking my things I decided to go and find my bearings in the city. I walked through a tangle of streets, toward the docks, from where I would shortly be leaving. The air of the town changed abruptly as I got nearer the sea: you could sense it out there, almost taste it, even if you couldn't see it. The two mythical Liver birds loomed out through the dusk: the one – as I later found out – facing out to sea to watch over sailors, the other protecting the city.

I got as close I could, up to the wire fence which seemed to stretch for miles; just beyond this, the ghostly hulls of cargo ships rose like giant headstones, obscuring the sea. A warden came along and ushered me from the area, so I returned by the same streets to my room in the lodging house, stopping only to chat with the proprietress and listen to her prescribed knowledge of the city. There was a small table in the room and some notepaper, headed with the name and a printed likeness of the house, and I sat and wrote letters to Irene and my parents. I stayed up smoking till the early hours, watching the slow clouds drift over the room – adding to the smoke of previous occupants which seemed to have suffused not only the wallpaper and bedding, but the air itself. Then, unable to sleep, I laid out my clothes for the following morning.

2

The ship that was to be my home for the next three years – for I was to spend more time at sea than not – was called the *Marianna*. Built in the late twenties, she had started life as a passenger ship; she had been involved in the evacuation of Western France after Dunkirk, helping Czechs, Poles and Free French to escape Nazi-occupied Europe. When she reached England, she was taken over as a troopship and would remain that way until after the war.

At first glance, she looked an impressive sight there in the docks: over 500 feet long with two large funnels and masts fore and aft, she looked as though she could hold her own in rough seas. But we were about to make the treacherous Atlantic crossing with U-boats to contend with.

Not designed for warfare, she had been hastily re-painted grey: you could still see the roller marks just above the waterline. Other modifications included an anti-submarine gun mounted on the stern and a machine gun for use against aircraft, but these would offer little resistance if the ship were travelling out of convoy.

I'd learnt enough on the training ship to feel justified in my misgivings, yet there were things other than the ship that contributed to this sense of unease; something to do with how desolate ports can look at morning: the filthy water, floating bottles and condoms, the scum left by the tidemark on the harbour walls, coupled with the faintly nauseous smell of rotting seaweed and sea and oil. In my mind, which was both tired and alert, the combination of these things seemed to equate with and point towards some kind of sordid death. The only fear I could put a name to, however, was the fact that I couldn't swim, something not uncommon back then. In the days leading up to my departure, Irene had tried to teach me at the local baths, without much success. Later, when I was on board the ship, some of the older sailors commented on the folds of skin and the extra gap between my toes – 'webbed feet, lad,' they said – which according to superstition meant that I would never drown.

I shook hands with some of the men, many looking as nervous as I was. The old lady was right – you could tell those who'd been to sea before from the novices – there was something written on their faces that gave you a feeling of assurance or otherwise. There were forty or so crewmembers – only a handful had sailed together before – but we bonded very quickly, you sought out the faces that looked confident, dependable – those were the ones you stuck by. We had gathered on deck to be addressed by the first mate; the captain was engaged in talks with the other heads of convoy. Our destination would be revealed once we had put to sea and in the meantime the ship was to be made ready for inspection. Sensing the mood was one of uncertainty, the officer – who was later to prove his expertise – tried to raise our morale: he told us that he'd 'served on many ships, some better, some worse' than the present one, but that 'it all depended on the unity of the crew.' An unbroken chain of command was the most important rule aboard a ship: orders had to be acted upon with the speed of nerve impulses; each crewmember functioned as 'vertebrae in a spinal column'; remove any one, and 'the vessel is disabled.' If this could be achieved to the highest degree, the ship would become 'something more than its iron and rivets.' Experience had taught him that 'the correct tactics outweighed the technical side,' and that, for much of the time, 'the U-boats would also be sailing blind.'

He spoke with an ardour for his subject which persuaded us that he at least was convinced of our chances, but as soon as he'd gone, the regular seamen resumed their duties with a resignation formed of habit, securing derricks and hatch covers, while the raw recruits, myself among them, scrubbed and scoured the deck around the main hatchway, which was black with the residue of some spilled cargo. We were still at this task, with our buckets and brushes, as the ship pulled out to sea. I looked up and saw the docks diminishing in the distance; in wartime, your choices and decisions were not your own – I couldn't believe how little control I had over my own fate.

The *Marianna* was bound for New York, and as we left the Irish Sea, there was time for some last minute preparations – a crash course in loading and firing the guns and lifeboat drills – before the most dangerous stretch of the journey – the Atlantic passage. We seemed to move slower in the daylight hours when in sight of the rest of the convoy; although we were escorted by two destroyers, the company of other ships – especially the labouring cargo-liners – always created the illusion of restricted movement and additional burden. Sometimes, we seemed to move as slowly as barges on a canal.

I started my navy career as an assistant steward: the outward passage would be comparatively easy as we would only have to cook for and serve the crew until we took on troops. The chief steward took us round the stores and explained the scale of provisions: the allowances of each man per week. These had been set out by the navy to ensure that everyone got his fair share of fresh meat and vegetables, but only lip service was paid to this in wartime. We often had to make do with oily fish – tinned herring and pilchards – as our main source of nutrition and this was to be a constant gripe for our 'passengers': American and Canadian troops accustomed to their wives' and mothers' home cooking.

The cold Atlantic waters brought heavy swells and my muscles soon ached from having to brace myself and compensate for the ceaseless rolling and pitching of the ship. After walking the decks in stormy seas, with heavy, cumbersome steps, the ache refused to leave my legs and became permanent; it made sleeping very nearly impossible. As I lay in my bunk at night and turned my face into the pillow, it seemed that I was looking into the depths of the sea, through the hold, through the hull, twenty metres down; I would lie there, half expecting an explosion to tear through the floor at any moment. There were times, as well, when I was afraid to sleep; as if by closing my eyes I would forfeit any measure of control over life and death.

At those times, I'd get up and talk to someone on watch; that was the best way, the only way to get away from the circumstances we found ourselves in, to talk of home, to bring out photos of wives, fiancées, girlfriends so we could forget where we were for a few moments. I became good friends with a deck officer called Charlie – he was one of those trustworthy faces I'd met on the first day. He'd been attacked at sea many times; once he'd been blown overboard by the force of an explosion and had to wait fourteen hours in the water before he was picked up; he considered himself lucky because many of those left onboard had perished. But he loved the sea and wanted to continue sailing after the war. He taught me a great deal about sailing and I think it was because of him that I survived those first few months at sea.

Sometimes I would join him for the middle watch, from midnight till four. Nothing can look so abyss-like, so much like a void, as the night seen from the deck of a ship far out at sea. I remember one night in particular when there was no light in the sky. Black clouds hid the moon and stars; the ship itself had been blacked out, and all I was aware of was the hulking motion of the ship and the shuddering of the engines – these things only told me that the ship was still moving. I remember losing all sense of dimensions and direction – we might have been at the bottom of the ocean, it was so dark – and I had to go to the bow to be sure, to see it cutting the phosphorescent surf from the black waters. Somewhere in that darkness, ahead and astern of the convoy, the destroyers were sounding the ocean with the Asdic sonar and dropping depth charges. I walked back down the ship. At the stern some seagulls were following us. They hovered above the deck, the beat of their greyish white wings more visible at night and ghostly in its effect.

There was really very little you could do if you fell into the path of one of the U-boats – a ship our size couldn't hope to outrun them – you'd be a sitting duck. With little to do except keep watch, eat and sleep, you'd think about ships that had been torpedoed, the crews that had drowned in that dreadful blackness.

When we finally reached New York, there was intense relief; it was as if we'd just walked through a minefield and emerged unscathed on the other side – I suppose in a way, we had. The Statue of Liberty, like some ancient goddess bestowing her protection on sailors, was there to see us in, and I found myself wondering whether she would extend us the same good fortune on our return home.

3

We had a day's shore leave before we took on troops – one day and one night before we would have to retrace our steps across the 'minefield'. Charlie couldn't wait to get ashore; he had been there before and knew his way round, so I decided to stick with him. We had shaved and spruced up, glad to leave the clamminess of our quarters and set foot again on dry land.

My eyes were so used to the monochrome of wartime Britain, that I was quite unprepared for the sights that awaited us in New York. Cars everywhere, with shiny chrome grills and bumpers, bright lights that glared after the blackouts back home. And as we walked, long-forgotten smells would come drifting across our path; there was rationing here as well, but not like we knew in Britain. We stopped at a café – or 'diner' as they were called – and drank the first decent coffee either of us had had for a long time – on the tables were what looked like salt shakers filled to the brim with sugar – there was even cream.

Charlie said: 'When you think of the shoe-scrapings that pass for tea and coffee back home, it makes you want to cry.'

'What do you want to do next?'

'I was thinking of buying a camera – I wanted to take some pictures for my wife.'

We bundled into a cab and asked to be taken to Fifth Avenue; the driver, having noted our accents, couldn't have been nicer – he embarked on a whirlwind tour of the city, pointing out buildings and landmarks that passed by in a flash – there was so much to take in. You knew you were somewhere different, you felt it immediately; the rhythm was different – it was fast and frenetic and it took a while to get used to. I'd never seen anything like it: the solid blocks of the towers blotting out huge sections of the sky – it seemed like we were riding round at the bottom of a shadowy canyon.

Charlie asked the driver where we could buy the camera and that reminded me that I needed to buy something for Irene, so we ended up at one of the big department stores. There was a black dress on one of the mannequins, but I couldn't find it hanging up anywhere, so I asked one of the pretty salesgirls who seem to populate such stores:

'Excuse me, do you have this dress in stock?'

'You're English?'

'Yes.'

'Would you mind repeating what you just said? I love hearing that accent.'

'Would you happen to have this dress? I'd like it for my fiancée.'

'What size is she?'

I had to confess that I didn't know. She told me not to worry: 'Point to someone who looks like her and I'll tell you her size straight off.' I looked around the store. Most of the women shopping there were older than Irene; some of them may well have been her size, but it was confusing. There was a girl on the cosmetics counter; she had blond hair, of which a few wisplike strands had strayed from the combed ones, and pale lips. She was about Irene's height and size, but it was something about her regard that recommended her, her way of not looking directly at anyone, while continuing to make her presence felt to customers in the store. I pointed her out discreetly, but my assistant called over to her: 'Hey, this gentleman says you look like his fiancée!'; the girl looked up from her counter and her pale face flushed a deep shade of red.

My assistant returned with the dress, and I watched her fold and wrap it. 'She'll love it!' she assured me. 'Have a safe trip back to England.' I thanked her. The exit was at the top of a small flight of stairs and when I was halfway up I turned and looked back over the heads of people and the racks upon racks of clothes to the pale girl on the make-up counter. I waited. Finally she looked up and her eyes met mine across the intervening distance, but this time she didn't blush. She smiled and I felt better than I'd done in a long time.

The Allied invasion, though expected on all sides, was still a few months off, but the massing of troops had begun: we took on American and Canadian soldiers as well as British and Canadian airmen who had been completing their flight training in the US and Canada. We made one more stop, at Halifax, Nova Scotia, before heading back across the North Atlantic. The sea was freezing and a wreath of icicles had formed around the rail at the bow.

The *Marianna* could carry 720 passengers, but we had far exceeded that number on our return voyage: the men were crammed into every available cabin and we had our work cut out to accommodate them all. Some preferred to sleep out in the corridors where it was less cramped and you'd always be tripping over someone's mattress or feet as you made your way round the ship.

The voyage seemed to last an eternity, each wave that broke on the ship slowing us a little, dragging out the waiting time that lay between us and home.

The boredom and restlessness that we had felt on the outward voyage now transferred itself to the troops we were carrying: with little to do, no outlet for their energies or desires, they took out their frustration on each other or the crew. The military discipline which had been instilled in them in training was already starting to crumble: there was one bad fight in the saloon where someone was glassed in the face and required stitches from the ship's surgeon. And we were given the ominous task of separating them without becoming embroiled ourselves.

But it wasn't always possible; there were some remarks that you just couldn't ignore. On one occasion, a soldier passing the open door of my cabin had eyed the picture of Irene I kept on my wall and said 'How much is it for a turn with her?' I lost my head and grabbed him by the collar, taunts flying all the while; luckily, one of his mates stepped in between us saying: 'Save it for the Germans!'

For some time, there had been a growing swell, lifting the ship like an invisible hand. Gradual at first, the *Marianna* began to pitch at a sharper and sharper angle until plates and cutlery went crashing down from the tables, glasses shattered and splintered. 'This should sort the men from the boys,' I heard one man utter, but he was only a boy himself. By the following day, the sky had darkened; the horizon blotted out by low scudding clouds. On the stairs, I met the bosun, breathing hard; he was going round the ship, making sure that everything was secured and fastened down, and he sent me to check the galley.

It was a mess: someone had forgotten to latch the cupboard and there were pots and pans clattering around the floor. I'd just finished stowing the last of them when the cook appeared, looking the worse for wear. He took the lid off one of the large stockpots and the produced a sizeable bottle of rum: 'Got a secret stash,' he said, touching his nose. 'Here y'are lad. Get this down ya.'

'What about the chief steward?' I said warily.

'That's the good thing about storms – no one comes in here.'

The harsh brown liquid burned my throat as it went down, but was pleasantly warming. The cook solemnly raised his glass in a toast to the storm.

As I went round the ship, I became accustomed to seeing the pallid white faces of those struck down by seasickness; later, when we came to serve the evening meal, the mess hall was virtually empty. The cook was right – it made our job easier: when I told him, he laughed and said 'Well they owed us a Bank Holiday.'

For the next two days, the storm raged: with the wind whipping spray across the decks, the *Marianna* would lurch from side to side, up and down, rolling and pitching at the same time.

Such conditions made even the simple act of walking near nigh impossible; you'd constantly be having to brace against the next wave, trying to move in time to the rhythm of the sea. It was like following the steps of a complicated dance; after a while, you became more adept, but there would always be one freak wave – *a jarring note* – that would trip you up when you least expected.

It was on the second day, when the storm reached its height: we were pitching at an alarming angle. I was bending to retrieve the keys to the store when suddenly, I felt my feet leave the floor; I was catapulted backwards, then everything went black. When I came to, my head was reeling and the side of my face was numb. Struggling to open my eyes, I clung to the window ledge and tried to stand. The ship toppled again, but before she could rise, the next wave broke, submerging the bow; and for a moment, all you could see was the cruciform shape of the mast standing above the spray.

4

I'm sorry I broke down last time – it was the drink that did it. Please apologise to Irene for me and tell her not to worry.

We'd just got back and I was reading through the stack of letters that had built up; I used to help the chief steward sort the mail, one of the benefits being that I could collect mine first. There were letters from Irene and Mother, but for some reason I'd opened Geoff's first: I suppose I had more reason to worry about him given the dangers he faced. He had talked about his birthday – he'd made it back home in the end – but I wasn't prepared for what came at the end of the letter. What did he mean? It made me all the more anxious to get home and find out what had happened since I'd been away.

To my surprise, we'd been granted a few days' leave – it was unusual to get home leave so early – but then we'd have to pay it back next time; there'd been rumours that we were for the East, which meant we wouldn't see home again for some time.

At Lime Street, the platforms were heaving with men in uniform: my black eye – now swollen into a slit I could scarcely see through – and the angry purplish bruise on my cheek drew a good many stares, some clearly impressed – it was a badge of honour, no matter whether it was a war wound or the result of a pub brawl.

I boarded the train and could only get standing room in the corridor until we had gone a few stops and things started to clear. I found a seat in a compartment opposite a middle-aged woman in a feathered hat and tatty fox-fur and a censorious-looking old man; my face must have given them a fright – they exchanged quick glances and shifted in their seats. I could see the dreadful possibilities running through the woman's mind until she noticed the MN badge on my lapel. The old man evidently had not seen it; I knew what he was thinking: 'Why isn't a young man your age in uniform?' I could have cursed the Merchant Navy, we were the only one of the services without a uniform – and were often seen as the poor relation of the Navy proper.

'Bad storm at sea,' I started to explain.

Reassured the woman asked me where I was from and started telling me about her son who was around the same age; the old man asked me:

'Can you tell us where you've been or aren't you supposed to say?'

And so the journey passed agreeably enough, but what I really wanted was to be left alone to read my bundle of letters. After a while, they got off and were replaced by a young soldier who was far less inquisitive: smelling strongly of whisky, he pulled down his cap and fell asleep almost immediately. I took out the letters and scoured each one for clues as to what might be wrong, but found nothing: Irene had written that she'd 'managed to get together the ingredients for Geoff's birthday cake' – she'd once told me that all the girls who worked at the cake factory would hide lard and sugar in their bras and up their sleeves – it was one of the 'perks' of the job.

As the train pulled into Smethwick, I breathed a sigh of relief: the old station was still standing. I went into one of the shops across the road and bought cigarettes and some peppermint creams for my mother and with my kitbag slung over my shoulder, the box with Irene's dress under one arm, I made my way home, changing my route slightly to take in the Accles and Pollock factory. I just wanted to check that Dad was ok; he'd be there working on tubing for the guns. I carried on round West Smethwick Park, then down Manor Road. There were a couple of bomb-damaged houses that had been shored up, you could see inside like a doll's house: the roof and front wall had gone and the wallpaper was streaked with red brick dust which had bled into the pattern from exposure to the rain. The damage wasn't recent; they had been that way before I left and were unlikely to be repaired any time soon, but it still gave me a start and made me quicken my step.

There's that moment when you turn into your own street and your heart misses a beat: you're almost too frightened to look. But then you turn the corner and you see that it's all still there just as you left it.

And it was good to be back in the house where I'd grown up: the mint green stripes Father had painted in the kitchen, the gas cupboard where he kept his box accordion and the leather strap on a hook to sharpen his razor, the larder where Mother kept her cakes and lard on the cold slab. All still there.

But I was now terribly aware of my brother's absence. When I'd been at home with my parents waiting for him, it had been different. I think now

I'd seen active service I was doubly aware of the dangers he faced and I wished more than ever that the war would be over.

In the living room, my eye was immediately drawn to his portrait – as with the rest of the things in the house, I seemed to notice it more than before. But now my Navy portrait stood next to it – Father must have framed it while I was away. It was strange to see them side by side and it didn't seem quite right: Geoff was much braver and I wondered whether I warranted equal place there.

My mother came in and seeing me holding Geoff's portrait, smiled. 'I'm so glad your brother was able to get back for his birthday – at one point, we didn't think he would. I only wish you'd been here as well.' She ran her fingers through my hair and let her hand rest on my shoulder.

She brought out his letters and read me his latest one; it began: *I'm still alive and kicking after another long night over the Third Reich. Last night I had the best take-off ever; there was a crowd there to see us off…*

He'd written about the group of WAAFs who gathered at the side of the runway to wave him off; before his last 'trip' they'd all kissed him and he'd flown over the Third Reich covered in lipstick.

He'd signed off: *You can read about me in the paper!* – and Mother had duly collected the cutting: on the date the letter was postmarked there had been a raid on Essen, right in the heart of the Ruhr, the Krupps Works. He must have written the letter the next morning.

I laughed, but it wasn't the same as having him back.

'I suppose you want to go and see her,' said Mother, reading my mind. 'Go on then, but don't be too long if you want to see any of that rhubarb tart.'

I arrived at the factory twenty minutes early and stood by the gates waiting for Irene to appear. Feeling nervous, I smoked a cigarette; that letter – *please apologise to Irene* – was still playing on my mind. What did he have to apologise for?

It seemed to take forever to get around to six o'clock, but finally I heard the whistle blow and droves of factory girls started making their way out, still in their white overalls. A security guard was on the gates, eyeing them suspiciously; he took one of them aside and had her empty her pockets. While this was going on, Irene and two of her friends walked quickly towards the gate, but not without escaping the attention of the guard who shouted

'Oi, hang about!' Irene turned with one of her dazzling smiles and said 'I've got to go home and do my hair. You haven't forgotten our date, have you?' The girls she was with laughed and the man laughed too.

Again, suspicion crossed my mind, but it evaporated when I saw how pleased she looked to see me; she ran and flung her arms round me.

'What happened to your eye?'

'I had a bit of a bust-up with a metal door – the door came out of it better than I did.'

She smiled incredulously: 'Are you sure it wasn't a bust-up in a bar?' She caught sight of the box under my arm: 'Is that for me? Can I open it now?'

A group of girls had gathered round to watch her – as she held up the dress and it unravelled against her, they sighed in approval.

'I hope you're going to let me borrow it,' said one.

'The dress or the boyfriend?' said another and they fell about laughing.

'It's perfect,' Irene said. 'How did you know my size?'

Later, as we walked back to my parents', I asked her about Geoff's letter – I could see she didn't want to tell me, but I pressed her:

'I'd arranged a party for him, at the Blue Gates. I know one of the barmaids and she knows Geoff as well – she let us have the room upstairs, I think she'd have done pretty much anything for him!

'I brought my records and so did Rita, we had *You'll never know, In the Mood* … and I'd been dancing with him …'

Again, I felt my stomach twisting in knots as I tried to keep my jealousy from surfacing.

'All our friends were there; the men were all in uniforms and suits and ties and I'd invited some of the girls from work. We were having a wonderful time and I was so glad Geoff had managed to get home on leave, but at some point, I lost him. I went round asking everyone "Where's Geoff gone?", but no one had seen him. Eventually, me and Rita left the others and went to look for him; we went downstairs to see if he was outside and there he was on the stairs, crying, really crying. It *shook* me – I'd never seen him like that before.

'I didn't know what to think. Rita and I looked at each other as if to say "Is he drunk?", but I'd been dancing with him all evening and I knew he hadn't drunk that much. So we sat on the stairs and put our arms round him and Rita said "What's the matter?" And he just said "I don't want to go back."'

I felt a chill run through me; and I remembered he'd said the same thing on the night I met Irene at the dance – the exact same words: *I don't want to go back*. Before, whenever his leave was up, he'd simply shrugged and said 'Well, I've got to go back I suppose. See you in a couple of months.' But this was something different.

'Did he say why?'

'I'm not sure exactly – he said there'd been one mission where they'd had a close call – but he wouldn't tell me what happened.'

'Poor Geoff,' I thought to myself, and then I felt terrible for having been jealous of him. I said to Irene 'He'll be alright', trying not to show how much it had affected me. But I meant it. *He had to be alright* – I didn't want to think about the alternative.

5

Irene came back with me – Mother had the tea on the table and Father had opened a bottle of his sloe gin – he made this lethal concoction in a still down the garden. By the time we'd finished eating, the bottle was considerably depleted and Father was singing at the top of his voice; Mother kept saying 'Shush or you'll wake the neighbours!' In the end, she sent him up to bed like a naughty child.

'Shall we help him up the stairs?' Irene said.

'No, let him do it himself,' Mother replied, 'if he falls and breaks his neck, it's his own fault.'

I'd drunk a few glasses myself and thought I'd better take Irene home while I could still walk ok.

I had made up my mind already that I wanted to marry her – I'd even begun saving for a ring, intending to do things properly. But as I walked her home that night, I felt an added sense of urgency. In a few days' time, I'd be back again on that ship, heading God knows where and for how long. But it was more than that. Irene was so attractive that men vied for her attention even when I was with her – I was afraid she'd be snapped up by someone else.

I walked her to her door and we kissed goodnight – she pulled away sooner than I did. I knew it wasn't the right moment, but emboldened by alcohol, the words were already half out:

'What if we got married?'

I could see straightaway that it hadn't worked; my words had failed to hit the mark.

'I don't know what to say …' she was shaking her head.

'You don't want to.'

'It's not that, it's all happening so quickly, I just don't know.' She saw the look of disappointment on my face: 'I'm sorry, it's just a lot to take in, that's all.'

I wanted the ground to swallow me up and was grateful when she brought things to a swift conclusion:

'Let's not see each other tomorrow – I need some time to think.'

It sounded like the truth – maybe she just needed time – but it still felt like a rejection and the pain it caused was no less great.

The bottle of gin was on the sideboard, incredibly some still left in it; I emptied it into a glass and sank down on the sofa. I wasn't sure if the alcohol had made things better or worse – worse, probably. Why had I asked her? I knew why, of course: I thought about her all the time, first thing in the morning, last thing at night. But she was out of my league. Why had I allowed myself to think I stood a chance with her?

The next day I slept late; even with everything that was going on, I'd managed to sleep well – it was being back on dry land, without the ground rocking and reeling all the time.

All day, I resisted the urge to go and see Irene; we'd previously made plans to go out that evening, but I no longer knew how things stood. I wondered what Geoff would have done in the same situation – he'd never had to chase after girls, it was usually the other way round. So that was that, I decided – it was up to her now to make the next move.

That evening was quite like old times: my father and I peeling spuds and shelling peas, the old enamel pot in front of us, under the watchful eye of my mother.

Dinner over, my mother said: 'Not going out tonight, then?'

Once the blackout curtains were up, the old man brought out his box accordion and gave us his 'Lili Marlene'; we didn't listen to the wireless that much in the evening – not the news anyway: the reports on allied bombing upset Mother. Of course, it was worrying for all of us – we didn't know what raids Geoff was on – we could only guess from the 'clues' in his letters – he would say things like *I hope you had a nice weekend – I did, over the Third Reich* – and I'd try to piece these snippets together with the scant information available in the newspapers and on the radio.

I looked at the clock – half past ten – he could well have been heading out over the North Sea, across the heavily defended Dutch Coast …

When he'd last come home, at the end of January, he'd told me about the first two ops he'd flown with his new Squadron – the target for both had been the same, and one of the most dangerous of the war: Berlin. He'd literally come home directly after the last of these; his face still wore the tension of the previous night as he relived the raids:

'It was nearly all over before it began – on our very first op, I heard the words: "The target for tonight is Berlin", you saw the expression change on the faces around you. The Squadron Leader pulled back the curtain – there was the map with a red string from our base right into the heart of the Third Reich. You're prepared for anything, but it still gets you here' – he pointed at his throat: 'It was like the air had been sucked out of the room.'

He paused; for a moment, it seemed as if the memory had overwhelmed him. Then he said:

'We had problems right from the start: there was a terrible cranking noise – the undercarriage hadn't retracted properly and the drag it created meant that we fell behind the rest of the stream and were thrown off course …'

He shook his head in disbelief: 'We were basically flying a crippled aircraft – it would have been a suicide mission if we'd continued. We'd gone the long way round, over Denmark, to put us out of range of the night-fighters – we'd already used a lot of fuel and we used up even more correcting faults. I realized we wouldn't have enough to get back, so I got on the intercom to the skipper … he wanted to carry on, but eventually he saw sense and we ditched the bombs.

'We were the last back – we were so far off course that I think we were over Lithuania at one point – it was thanks to the navigator that we got back at all, I don't know how he worked out our position.

'On the way to the debriefing with the Senior Intelligence Officer, we met another crew coming out: "Well, I never," said the Mid-Gunner, "it's B for Beer – we'd given you up for dead."

'I explained what had happened. But as we went in, I heard him whisper to his mate: "The buggers got off lightly."

'"Lightly!" I thought, "we could have crashed on the runway," but then I realized he was probably right – a lot of chaps never came back from that raid.'

He lit a cigarette and inhaled deeply: 'And then two nights later, it was Berlin again.'

This time, they'd reached the target: 'There wasn't as much flak as we were expecting – they probably hadn't counted on us coming back so soon – we hadn't ourselves. I could hear the Bomb-Aimer over the intercom:

"Right, right-right, keep it steady, steady … bombs gone!" And the aircraft suddenly lifts like an escaped barrage balloon – that's when you know the thousand-pounders have gone. As he took the target photograph, I heard the Aimer say: "That should please the intelligence officer. He likes holiday snaps – especially the Berlin ones.'"

I suddenly remembered that I hadn't finished reading his letters from the day before: I glanced through the postmarks to find the ones written since I'd been away and started to read; one of them was about me:

Have you heard from my brother yet? Don't worry, God will bring him back alright. We have a box in the Mess for the 'Merchant Navy' and everyone I meet I tell them to put some money in because it's for a good cause, I tell them that I have a brother in it and that they should be thoughtful of those fellows who have to go out and bring their food and stuff back for them, and don't you know we get lots of money in it, and I'll see we continue to do so too.

After reading that, there was nothing I could say; even if he'd decided to run off with Irene, I could probably have forgiven him.

Another day went by and still Irene didn't come; I'd almost given up hope and resigned myself to going back without seeing her again. Then, on the night before I rejoined my ship, I heard someone tap the window three times: thinking it was a warden, my eyes travelled automatically to the blackout cover; the one on the top right always managed to work itself loose somehow – if they spotted even a chink of light, there'd be hell to pay. I braced myself as I opened the door, but instead of the warden, there was Irene, looking more beautiful than ever.

'Yes,' she said, 'The answer's "yes."'

I knew even then that she didn't love me as I loved her, but I wasn't about to talk her out of it: life without her would have been unthinkable.

6

'Whatcha gonna get up to, then, when you're back in Civvy Street?'

'Marry Irene.' Hearing myself say those words, I still couldn't quite believe it. Like it might all be a dream.

'Ah, that girl of yours.' The cook laughed mischievously: 'Let's hope she can wait that long.'

'What do you mean?'

'I mean it's a long way to the East and back. A girl can get lonely. A man can too, when it comes to that.'

That evening, as I lay in my bunk, I wondered whether I should have told him. When you tell people something like that, it makes it official, gives it an air of 'certainty'. But can you really be certain of anything in a war? Maybe it was tempting fate, making plans like that – I couldn't even be certain that Irene wouldn't change her mind.

But the next day I thought 'Maybe I'm being too superstitious' – it could do that to you, being in the war.

This time, our passage would take us through Suez – the rumours, for once, had turned out to be true.

We headed out into the Atlantic, turning south, through the Straits of Gibraltar and along the North African coast up to Port Said – the gateway to Suez and the East.

As we waited our turn to enter that narrow waterway, we were besieged by small boats selling fruit – the kind of fruit you could only dream about – we'd never had such fruit in Britain, not even before the war. We lowered down the money in buckets and hauled up the fruit, as if we were drawing water from a well.

From then on, the temperature seemed to increase, the baking sun reflecting off the desert sands on either side of the Canal. Heat haze on the horizon. I saw a man on a camel stop to watch us go past: a ship the height of three houses stacked on top of each other gliding through the desert.

At Bitter Lakes, the halfway point, the water broadened out like an oasis – the whole thing shimmering in the heat:

'I'm still dreaming,' I thought. 'Any moment now, I'm going to wake up.'

Stopping in Aden to refuel, we heard reports of D-Day – the terrible loss of life in the sea and on the beaches. But it was a turning point – it would only be a matter of time now.

As we set sail for Burma, some of the crew were predicting we'd be home in time for Christmas. But I noticed Charlie was very quiet.

On deck, it was a bit like a Bank Holiday in Blackpool: the troops rolled up their trousers and tied handkerchiefs over their foreheads while they lolled in the sunshine. It was easy to forget the war – that sultry heat went straight to your head, you could get drunk on it.

But one morning our peace was broken by the distant humming of a plane; it was quite far off and high up, like a great silver bird. It passed by on a straight course and didn't come back round.

'One of ours?'

'I doubt it, not in this neck of the woods.'

'B-17?'

'It's difficult to tell at that altitude.'

'You did do the aircraft recognition course, I trust?'

'I shouldn't listen to him – he doesn't know his arse from his elbow.'

And then a voice behind us abruptly ended the debate:

'It was a reconnaissance plane.'

We all turned round – it was Charlie: 'They're taking note of our position.'

'I reckon they didn't see us.'

'Oh they saw us alright.'

That night we stayed up playing cards, even those who didn't normally play.

'Do I have to explain the rules again? It's like this …'

It was anyone's game that night – no one was really concentrating on the cards. We were all listening intently for a sound that could not be heard – a torpedo cutting through the water. Eventually, we drank ourselves to bed.

It only takes a day or so – perhaps not even that long – to lull yourself into a false sense of security. We had met neither surface craft nor U-boats – perhaps they hadn't seen us after all, or else they'd gone after some other poor bastards.

We had our usual Friday night singalong – strange how we still looked on it as the weekend, how we clung to any semblance of our old lives.

I was down for a watch that night, but had scarcely got up from the table when the whole room shook – just before – or was it after that? – there was a screeching sound, the sound of displaced air. I remember thinking 'I don't want it to end like this – I need to see them all again.'

We were being attacked by a submarine – it had surfaced and was firing overwater shells. A shouting match ensued: orders were volleyed back and forth, I could feel the old passenger ship trying to turn as sharply as it could, to narrow the target as we pulled hard to starboard, churning up the sea. But the shells were getting closer; they fell with ever greater accuracy, raising great columns of water – it looked like a waterfall in reverse, there was something monstrous about it, unnatural. And then one fell on the deck; it detonated and bits of metal accelerated through the air, tearing through flesh and bone, whatever stood in its path. We fell to the ground and when we got up – we were on adrenalin, the sound seemed to have vanished, for a few moments it was like being in an invisible bell jar, and then it erupted again, back into sound. We were returning fire and then the enemy craft submerged, though we hadn't appeared to hit it. We kept our gun trained on where it had slipped underwater, we kept firing relentlessly at that piece of water. It was chaos, utter chaos. And then, a few seconds of calm; I realized that some of the sailors hadn't got up after the explosion, there were bodies on the deck – you could see instantly that they were dead.

Orders were now being relayed to keep eyes and guns trained on the sky in case of an attack from the air.

Hours passed and still we kept to the decks; fear kept us there, the fear we all felt, but wouldn't admit to. The bodies of the men were laid out – men that had been walking only hours before, men we all knew. Their eyes were still open, and we covered them where they lay, with coats at first; later, they were wrapped in canvas. We stood around the funnel as if for warmth or protection from the elements though the night wasn't cold. We might have been keeping a vigil for the dead men, but in truth, none of us could have slept. The deck was littered with debris and charred, twisted metal and the ship seemed newly fragile, as if it too had sustained its wounds.

We waited, expecting the explosion from a torpedo to tear through the deck. But the attack never came.

The next day we all gathered for the burial at sea; the scene couldn't have been more different from the previous night's terrors: the sea blue and serene, with glints of light sparkling on the waves, as if someone had broken a mirror and scattered the pieces over the ocean. The service was brief and the convoy kept moving; we couldn't stop, for fear of further loss of life; there had been reports of surface craft still in the area and it felt like we couldn't pay our respects to the men, the war was unforgiving in that way. No time to grieve or pause for reflection, no time even to collect your thoughts.

Then just before the committal, something happened that would cast a shadow over the days to come. Two sharks appeared out beyond the wake of the ship, their fins cutting in and out of the water; Charlie told me that he had seen this before, that they would surface just before a burial at sea.

It was possible of course that the sharks had picked up the scent of blood when the decks were washed down, but the timing had been so chilling that I was convinced they knew someone on board had died and were following in wait.

We knew we'd been lucky, those of us who'd survived: they must have run out of torpedoes or we'd never have lived to tell the tale. We limped back into Aden, where we were given some shore leave while repairs were carried out on the ship.

I was helping the chief steward with the mail. 'One for you here, mate, posh writing!' It was from Father, who only ever added postscripts to Mother's letters. My head spun – I knew what it was. 'You alright, fella?' Lionel called after me.

I walked out on deck and clumsily tore open the envelope: Geoff was missing after a raid, but I was to keep my hopes up. The old man's normally perfect writing was shaky. I kept telling myself: 'He'll be ok – he'll have bailed out, even if he's been captured, it'll be over soon' – as if it all might still turn out alright.

But by the time I got home again, my parents had already received the news we'd all been dreading: Geoff had been killed in a raid on Amiens, during the night of 12/13 June. There had been two survivors – the Rear and Mid-Upper Gunners had managed to bail out – but Geoff and the others had gone down with the plane.

I thought we might never know any more than that, but then, six months later, in January '45, we received a letter in French, along with a translation from the Air Ministry …

Part IV:

March 1970

1

～⚬❀⚬～

'Do you still have it?' said Sarah.

'Yes, we kept all the letters – it should be in a tin, in that suitcase there.'

Crumpled, the pages held together by a rusty staple, it had been written twenty-five years ago by a member of the Resistance who had found Geoff's plane and buried the bodies. Sarah started to read – she read it aloud – and I could see in her face the same emotions I'd felt when I read the words:

> *It was during the night of the 12/13 June, about 2am, that the plane, already damaged and being pursued by German fighters, crashed on the outskirts of our village. Two of the occupants had been able to jump out by parachute, but the fate of their comrades was more unfortunate and they crashed with their plane to the ground.*
>
> *In my capacity as leader of the local Resistance movement, and helped by my son Jacques, we were able to bury the bodies, each one wrapped in a flag and each in a proper coffin. This was done, in spite of German orders forbidding such procedure, and the Germans were kept in ignorance of the identity and number of the victims.*
>
> *Orders had been issued by the local German commanding officer (at Beauvais) that all the bodies were to be placed in one large coffin and placed in the ground where they lay with the notice "Here lie American soldiers".*
>
> *These orders were, of course, not carried out, and thanks to the two survivors (whom I was able to shelter for 15 days after the accident and finally lead to safety, under the very noses of the Germans), we were able to identify the bodies, a sad experience for them both. It was on 15th June that the religious service was celebrated, amidst a considerable crowd from the whole of the surrounding countryside; the flowers were so numerous that carts were needed to carry them to the graveside.*

> *Some days after the funeral, the Germans learned of the ceremony and were on the point of taking hostages for punishment, some of whom were called before the German Headquarters, when other more important events intervened …*

Sarah picked up the photo enclosed in the letter; it showed the wooden crosses which had marked the graves of the airmen until they were replaced by the white War Graves headstones.

'It must have been awful for Grandma – I don't think she ever got over it. I wish I'd shown her more affection – like I did with Gramps. If I'd understood more what she'd been through … but you don't when you're a child. I remember her crying, at Christmas, on birthdays. I always thought I'd done something wrong. But Gramps would just say "It's alright, she's just having a bad day." Did they ever visit his grave?'

'No, and we never had the money. I was in hospital all those years and then it was difficult to get a job 'cause no one was willing to take a risk on me.'

'You know, when I was younger, I felt I didn't really know you, like there was some part of you that you always kept hidden. But I understand now why you didn't want to talk about it.'

'I should have told you sooner.'

'We should visit his grave. One day, we'll go, we'll go together.'

2

❦

'We'd better get back,' I said, 'your Mother will be wondering where we've got to.'

Everything was packed up now – I'd never seen the house so empty – my parents had lived there since before I was born. But perhaps we had needed to clear everything away – all the things accumulated in the years since his death – so we could focus solely on him.

Sarah held the door while I tried to shift the box containing the old man's tools – it weighed a ton: there was a vice which obviously belonged to a factory, every kind of chisel you could imagine. I was soon out of breath.

'Here, let me help you.'

We shunted it together, then lifted it the last few steps into the back of the van I'd borrowed from my neighbour.

'You shouldn't be lifting things like that …'

'At my age?'

'You know what I mean.'

Sarah drove us home and I was glad she did – I felt exhausted.

Irene was at the window when we got back: 'I was getting worried about you.' I could tell she wanted to say something about it, but she waited until after Sarah had gone to bed.

'You were gone a long time with Sarah.'

'We talked.'

'What about?'

'About you – and the war.'

'What about me?'

'She was asking about our wedding – and Brixham. She'd been reading some of our old postcards.'

I could see Irene was avoiding my gaze. 'What did you say about Brixham?'

'I just told her about the beach and you nearly drowning yourself.'

Part V:

1949 – 1953

1

'Why don't you let me teach you?' she would always say after she'd been swimming.

And I'd say, 'I'd rather watch you,' which was partly true, but it was also because I hated the water, hated it as much as Irene loved it.

We'd had our wedding in Holy Trinity Church, where Irene and her younger brother had once taken shelter in the crypt from an air raid. She'd invited Sammy Wall, the warden who'd ushered them to safety, along to our wedding.

After the reception, we'd taken the train down to Brixham; the sun was shining and I felt that life had finally taken a turn for the better.

We stayed at the Watermans Arms, up in the high part of the town: because we were young and I'd been in the war, people would buy us drinks – we drank rough cider. The landlady, on hearing I'd been in the navy, regaled us with a hundred stories connected with the sea – like the time the town's fishing boats had been out in a storm, and the local women had taken any wooden items they could find – chairs, washboards, pails – and set fire to them on the quay to make a beacon.

I'd never seen Irene so happy, and I realized that it was being near the sea: she'd missed the lakes of her childhood.

Every morning, she'd go swimming; she'd put on her costume before we left, so as soon as we got to the beach, she could dive straight in.

One day, we went to Shoalstone beach; to get down to the sea, you had to clamber over rocks. The tide was going out, clawing at the shingle; the wind had got up and across the bay, you could see the waves crashing against the breakwater, threatening to engulf the tiny white lighthouse that stood at the end.

'You can't seriously be thinking of …,' but Irene was already making for the water:

'We've only got today and tomorrow left.'

And she'd gone in. As if to prove she could cope, she swam far out – much further than usual – around the rocks to the right of the beach. Then I lost sight of her.

The fear, the dread I felt was far worse than anything I'd felt before; my eyes were darting this way and that, frantically scouring the bay for any sign of her. I took off my shoes and still in my shirt and trousers, waded out until the water was up above my waist. I could feel it pulling my legs out from under me. Wave after wave, the sky and the sea merging, suddenly everything went up and down – I almost lost my balance …

Then I saw her: it looked as if she was being dragged out twice as far for each stroke she made to the shore. But she was a strong swimmer, Irene; even then I thought, 'She's never let anything get the better of her.'

When she got back to the shallows, she was shaking – I think she'd scared herself. I was livid: 'You could have bloody well drowned.' But she just laughed: 'You'd have rescued me, wouldn't you?'

'You know I hate the water.'

'I'm sorry.'

'Don't ever pull anything like that again.'

We made our way back up through the town, black clouds scowling down over the brightly painted cottages and guesthouses.

'Looks like it's down to stay,' said Irene.

'May as well go back to the room for a bit.'

'Oh yes? You've forgiven me, have you?'

We collected the key from the landlady and were heading up the stairs when we heard a man's voice:

'Are you the couple from the Midlands?'

'Yes.'

'The landlady mentioned there was another couple here on their honeymoon. I'm Frank – and this is my wife, Ann.'

He wasn't very tall, but nevertheless gave the impression of being tall – it was his physique. Taut and muscular, like a boxer. Handsome too. His wife looked familiar in some way, but I couldn't have said how I knew her.

I asked them where they were from – it turned out they lived over the other side of Smethwick. 'I expect you've met my wife already without knowing it,' he said smiling. 'She works on the buses.'

And suddenly I knew where I'd seen her: she was the conductress on the B83 – she usually wore her hair up under a cap.

'Small world, eh?' he said. 'Listen, I don't mean to impose, but do you want to join us for a drink? I bet we've got lots in common.'

It turned out that Ann was mad about tennis and it was agreed that we should have a doubles match the next day. That night I prayed to the rain gods to cancel it – I'd never been much good at tennis – only dancing – and I didn't want to make a fool of myself. But it wasn't just that: I hadn't liked the way he'd been looking at Irene – and she at him.

Our last day: it had drizzled through the morning, but just as we were about to give up on the whole idea, the sun finally put in an appearance. As the least experienced player, I was paired up with Ann, the strongest, and he with Irene.

'Just get the ball back over the net,' said Ann as I got ready to return service, 'and I'll do the rest.'

We quickly took the lead, despite my ineptness; she was every bit as good as her husband had claimed. Frank was joking in a self-deprecating way: 'I didn't even see that one' – I could tell Irene liked him. I remember at one point, they both went for the ball at the same time and sort of brushed together; she almost went over, but he grabbed her around the waist and held her for a moment – they were both laughing.

He swapped addresses with us and we saw them three times after we got back home – the first time, they came round together, but then just him. And then he stopped coming and I forgot about them.

2

*

It wasn't long after we got back from the honeymoon that I started to feel seriously unwell.

The cough I'd had for a while – the doctor said I had an infection and gave me some antibiotics and it had disappeared, only to come back again after a few weeks. 'Fetch it up, son,' people would say to me when I was out on the horse and cart doing the milk round, or 'You'll cough your lungs out if you're not careful.'

'Perhaps I'd better pay you now,' one woman had said, 'sounds as if you might not be here tomorrow, love.'

But the cough I could live with. What was more alarming was that I'd begun to lose weight – that was part of the reason why I hated going on the beach, why I'd kept my shirt on throughout that holiday. Put me next to Frank, or any other man, come to that, and I looked like a bag of bones.

Looking back I probably should have got a second opinion, but I had other worries – we needed money. All those men back after the war looking for jobs and with the country in the state it was in … it was difficult at first to find work.

We were still living with my parents and Irene wanted a place of our own – I did too, I suppose.

I was glad to be home, but it made me sad too: everything in that house reminded me of Geoff. Sometimes when I was up in our old room – his cuff-links still on the shelf, the cigarette burn on the mattress which had got him into so much trouble with Mother – it was almost impossible to accept that I'd never see him again.

I got an evening job as a petrol-pump attendant and for a while I was doing two jobs until the milk depot cut back on staff: they'd converted to vans and I heard later that they'd slaughtered all the old horses, mine included.

Irene, meanwhile, was working as an usherette at the Prince's Cinema; the pay wasn't very good, but the manager would give her free tickets: some she'd sell cheap to our neighbours or we'd go ourselves. I can still remember the films she took me to see; we usually sat in the upper circle, on the edge of the balcony, and from time to time, I would glance across at her to see her reaction to the film.

The cinema had started out as a theatre; it still had the faded velvet seats and the decorative mouldings on the ceiling and balconies. Once, when the lights came up at the end of the film, we went down and looked at the stage with its proscenium arch; she told me that her mother had performed on that stage in music hall twenty years before. 'That was why she was so pleased when my father bought her the piano,' she explained. After that, whenever we went to the cinema, I thought of her mother singing there years before.

I used to worry about her walking home at night; there was a long alley behind the cinema – no street lights – and if she'd stayed behind to clean up and the foyer doors were locked, she had to walk down that alley alone. As soon as I finished at the garage, I would cut across by the canal path – a short cut – to try and meet her.

But one night I felt so tired that I wondered whether I'd be able to keep that appointment. I remember saying to myself 'One foot in front of the other' – I felt slightly feverish.

It was late, past eleven: I took the short route by the canal. There were no lights along the bank, only the headlights of cars passing over the bridges. The water had a strange lucidity, reflecting the black branches of trees though the water itself was black. I staggered on. The darkness, the night had taken the colour out of everything. I'd never felt so tired before.

A car passed slowly over a low bridge ahead, visible only by its headlights which appeared to float unattached in the darkness. Then I started coughing and I could taste something in my mouth; I knew the taste before I realized what it was. I quickened my pace. The canal lay still as a mirror, black shadows down one side of its length. I climbed the steps at the bridge and went and stood under a streetlamp. There, in the pool of light, I touched a finger to my lips, held it out and saw the colour of blood against my skin – it was unmistakably blood.

I was in a daze after that. I kept walking, but by the time I got to the High Street, the cinema was closed and there was no sign of her. When I got home, Irene was already asleep, but I was afraid to lie next to her and I slept on the sofa.

3

I kept it to myself for another day or two, but you can only deceive yourself for so long – after reaching the point of near exhaustion, there was no way I could carry on.

In a way, it was relief to find out what it was – to get the diagnosis of TB. At least that way, you know what you're up against.

Things moved pretty quickly after that: I was kept in hospital, on an isolation ward with six or seven other poor buggers whose coughs seemed even worse than mine. I would have to have a lung operation, they told me; it had spread so far that they'd have to remove one lung to give the other a chance of responding to treatment.

Irene told me that some men in overalls had been round to fumigate the house: the mattresses, the carpets – everything. 'At least you'll be safe,' I told her.

I'd seen some of my fellow-sufferers after they came back from their operations; there were tubes coming out of them and although our beds were screened from each other, I heard that some of them had died.

All operations were a risk then – this one especially so: they removed most of the one lung and there was a big cut right from the top of my shoulder down my back and around the ribcage. My chest was smooth on that side; to get at the lung, they'd removed some of my ribs, replacing them with a sheet of hard plastic; it always looked flat after, as flat as a table top, and I used to keep it covered up, even with Irene. I was in and out of consciousness for about a month. Irene told me later that she'd walked past my bed in the hospital; I was all swollen up, virtually unrecognizable – she had to go back to the duty nurse and ask what bed I was in.

At one point, they warned her that I might not make it. I don't remember much about it – apart from the pain – but I must have wanted to live.

Then one day, it felt like I was outside – the white walls of the ward were replaced by a different kind of white. White sky and white snow. I was vaguely aware of being lifted on a stretcher into the back of a waiting ambulance, the engine left running.

The ambulance men propped me up on pillows which took some of the pressure off my chest: I could see that snow had been heaped up to clear a path for the ambulance. I gradually realized that it was winter – that I'd lost two months in a state of unconsciousness since my operation.

4

Soon we were out in the countryside, the houses at the side of the road replaced by white fields. We passed an occasional farm building, a barn without a roof with snow falling through its exposed timbers. I didn't see any people. Through the frosted glass, it looked as if we were passing through a world cast in snow and ice. A crow which had been sitting on a telephone wire swooped down across the road and disappeared over one of the hedges, the only living thing in that winter landscape. The ambulance moved slowly; I could hear the tyres spinning, dredging up the snow. The engine cut and the driver swore softly: 'You'd better get him another blanket!'

It was silent without the engine, they seemed unsure what to do next. The silence became rather embarrassing and this must have prompted the driver to try again; he turned the key, and amazingly, the tyres caught. 'Bloody miracle!' he said. We passed over the top of the hill and turned down a narrow lane, brushing the snow from hedges at the side of the road. At last we came to a set of gates, imposing white gates, and we passed through.

The snow had been cleared from the drive and on either side I could see an embankment of pine trees. The doors were opened and I started shivering uncontrollably. They lifted my stretcher and carried me on a path that led through the trees, under swirling branches and swirling snow. I began to think it was a dream. Between the trees I could see the white walls of a building that seemed to merge with the snow. 'This is it,' said the driver, 'Romsley Sanatorium. We're going to take you straight to the ward.' It was a beautiful white building with tall gables that stretched right across the hillside. It had a large central section with a bell tower and a wing on each side. There were French windows on the ground floor, all of them open to let in the air; I imagined the sanatorium's inmates frozen into immobility. The windows on the upper floors had arches of purple brick set into the white facade, a wave of arches taking the eye across the length of the building. At first I thought the grounds were deserted, but then I saw that there were patients sitting out on the terrace, exposed to the elements.

They carried me through the French windows which were rattling in the wind. The ward where I found myself had six beds, with iron frames painted white, and there were glass screens between them. Plain white walls and ceilings. The patients were all young men, clad in pale striped uniform-like pyjamas. They looked thin and listless with shadows under their eyes, which were sunken in their faces. The only patient up and about was a man with wiry black hair and sharp features: his cheeks were hollow shelves and his angular nose his ruling feature. He was sitting at a table playing patience, laying out the cards not with enthusiasm, but in a stoical way as if this would do until he found some better way to pass the time. After the ward sister had explained the procedures he came across and shook my hand.

'I'm George, how are you doing? Don't worry, they'll soon have you up and about.'

'How long do you reckon I'll have to stay in bed?'

'That depends, you have to wait till the fever goes down. If it doesn't go down, they'll give your lungs a bit of a rest. "Pneumothorax", they call it.'

I'd heard of this: the lungs were collapsed by pumping air into the chest cavity; the thought made me shudder. Sensing my unease, he spoke reassuringly:

'You'll be alright – I've seen worse cases brought in here.'

'How long have you been here?'

'Seems like forever, but a little over five years, I'm one of the longest serving patients here, apart from the porter, the old chap who carried your bags.'

'He's a patient?' I said incredulously.

'Yes, they give you tasks to do as part of the treatment.'

He picked up the photo of Irene from the top of my bag and looked at it appreciatively: 'Wish I had a girl like that waiting for me at home.'

For the first few weeks, I was confined to bed; I had to lie in complete silence. All new patients had to go through this; any excitement or exertion was thought to interfere with the healing process. I spent the time adjusting to life on the ward. It was a strict place; there were rules and regulations to be followed, and the patients did this without question; I never heard any of them complaining. The nurses worked very hard; when they weren't looking after us, they would be cleaning; there was always an overpowering smell of disinfectant. During this time, I spoke to no one except the nurses who came round at regular intervals to take my temperature.

The Matron was a rather severe woman in a starched white gown, her silvery hair pulled tightly back under her white cap. She was like a hawk; nothing escaped her eye. There was not a speck of dust to be seen in the place; the floors were always spotlessly clean, the sheets on the beds neatly folded. If a patient coughed up blood, a nurse would be dispatched and the sheets would be changed and the area scrubbed and disinfected. The patients and nurses seemed to live in fear of her and I noticed that the atmosphere would become more relaxed whenever she left the ward. The younger nurses were more like us; we felt comfortable with them and we could share a joke together.

At last came the day when I was allowed to get up for the first time; I was unsteady on my feet and had to be supported by a nurse. It was as if my legs had forgotten how to walk, I couldn't support my own weight. My legs had absolutely no strength, no power at all. With the aid of the nurse, I managed to get once around the ward and then collapsed into a chair, completely out of breath. George came over to give me some moral support.

'I thought you said I'd be up and about in no time,' I said.

'I lied. Aren't you glad that I did? I had to say something to keep your spirits up.'

'My legs feel like they don't belong.'

'What you need is some breakfast – they do a first-rate breakfast here.' He went out into the corridor and brought back a wheelchair. A nurse was about to stop him, but he waved her away: 'I can manage, I'm not on my death bed yet.' He helped me into the chair and pushed me to the dining room at breakneck speed. This was the first time I had been off the ward since my arrival and it was good to get a change of scene and to have a friend in that place; I knew then that I would be able to cope with whatever lay ahead.

5

I soon became accustomed to life at the sanatorium, to the constant sound of coughing and the long periods of bed rest. The routine never changed and the patients just accepted it. I sometimes think it was their commitment to the routine – their belief in it – that kept them going rather than any of the medicine or treatment we received.

We were woken at six every morning with hot sweet tea and a thermometer. Then there would be steam baths. There was always a pungent smell of disinfectant and the bathrooms gleamed with light reflected from the shining metal surfaces and soap dispensers. After washing, we changed into fresh pyjamas; our old ones would be soaked in sweat as the fever was always worse during the night.

At eight, those of us who get could up went to the dining room for breakfast where they would feed us porridge, toast and marmalade and fresh fruit and make us drink a glass of milk. The food was very nutritious – a healthy diet was thought to be the best way of helping the body combat the disease. I knew I had to eat to get better and I tried to force myself, but it was all I could do to drink the milk and most of the food went untouched. I tried to make a show of eating for a kind young nurse called Dora. She always encouraged us to eat and she was so sad when we left the food that her eyes would moisten. She really cared about us. The nurses could see when we were getting thinner; not eating was a sign that the body was giving up on life.

After breakfast we would return to our beds and take the morning cure which consisted of fresh air treatment. That was the only way to treat the disease before streptomycin was discovered. We would lie in bed and the windows would be opened wide; the air was always redolent of the pine trees that surrounded the sanatorium. A period of silence would be enforced and we had to lie still in our beds without moving or talking while the nurses came round to check on us. The only sounds were coughing and the muffled laughter of patients sharing a joke, but the matron would say 'Quieten down!' I pulled my sheets up against the cold and looked out of the windows at the grounds. The snow glimmered in the winter sunshine; it was always very bright as our ward faced south to make the most of the sun. I longed to be able to get up and walk through the door, but after a while this desire left me as the disease took hold and my fever worsened.

The injections were the worst. At the time, they were carrying out trials with the new wonder drug, streptomycin, which would eventually provide the cure, although it was too late for many patients who were in the advanced stages of the disease or had already had lungs removed. They used to inject me in the hip with a large, thick needle; they had to throw it into us. It was very painful; one of the young doctors wasn't very good at giving injections and some of the patients would moan when he was on duty. But there was an older Scottish doctor who was more experienced; he used to 'flick' the needle so that the injection was relatively painless and everyone looked forward to the days when that doctor was on duty.

6

❧❦❧

'That's your daughter.'

I wiped my eyes; Irene was crying too.

Children weren't allowed on the ward, but my father had brought her into the grounds so I could see her from my bed. It was the happiest day of my life, but also one of the saddest: I knew I couldn't hold her – and might never be able to.

Irene came to visit me when she could, but of course she was even busier than before now that we had Sarah. I always looked forward to her visits – it was the one thing that kept me going. She always used to kiss me on the mouth when she came into the ward, even though this was frowned upon. I think she thought I'd lose heart. The other patients used to call out to her 'Where's my kiss?' and she would smile at them; she had a beautiful smile and I soon became an object of envy on the ward. Some of the wives wouldn't kiss their husbands at all because they were afraid of getting the disease, and I shared their concern; I was worried I might infect her:

'You shouldn't do that,' I told her.

'It's alright,' she said. 'I'm immune to it. I didn't tell you, but I had to go for a check-up. I went for an X-ray and they told me I'd had TB; I had the scarring on my lungs, but it had healed. I was lucky, I must have fought it off. The doctor told me I had a wonderful immune system.'

'I wish I had your immune system. Still, better to be safe.'

She was holding my hand on top of the blanket and I could feel her shivering; after a while she put her coat back on.

'It's like being outside with all the windows open,' she said. 'Don't they ever close them?'

'George told me that they used to close them during visiting times because some of the relatives complained, but they don't seem to bother anymore. It's probably safer to have them open, anyway.'

'I wish you could come home, I'm sure you'd be better off at home. We'd all look after you.'

'If I was well enough, I'd be there like a shot. But I'm fine, honestly. I'd be worrying about you all the time if I was at home. Here I can concentrate on getting well.'

'Your mother sent you some lemon cake, she's going to visit you on Thursday.'

'How are they?'

'They talk about you all the time.'

'Are you alright?'

She looked away. 'I'm changing my job, I've got a new job in a cake shop. The bakery was no good – they used to dock my pay when I took a day off to see you.'

'I wish I could be more help to you.'

'Don't worry about me.' She swiftly changed the subject. 'I went dancing last week. Your Dad said I needed a night off – he looked after Sarah.' She smiled: 'I wore that black dress you bought me.'

'Was it a success?'

'Yes, I danced with a handsome man all night.'

'Anyone I know?'

'You know I only go out with my friend from work. I danced with her; there weren't that many young men at the dance. We drank too much and on the way home, we danced all the way down the hill. We were in hysterics, we couldn't stop laughing. I haven't had fun like that for such a long time, I forgot about everything for a while.'

She looked desperately sad and I realized the effect my illness was having on her. She turned her face away.

'Don't cry, Irene. It'll be alright.'

'How can you be sure?'

'I just know. I've survived so far, I think it would have got me by now if it was going to get me.'

'You know, you have to get better, not just for me, but for Sarah. I don't want her to grow up without a father. You have to promise me you'll get well.'

'I'll do my best.'

She sat beside me on the bed and told me the news from home, and I watched the movement of her lips as she talked. I felt happy for a time. Then the bell signalled the end of visiting time and my eyes followed her to the door, where she turned and waved.

When the last of the visitors had gone, a silence descended over the place and we were left with our own thoughts. Would we ever go back to our families? Was it possible to recover? The course of the disease was unpredictable; sometimes a patient who seemed perfectly well would die the very next day. The visitors were also given false hope by the fact that there were few outward signs of the disease. At a glance, the patients seemed like any other young men; to hear them talk and laugh, you wouldn't have thought there was much wrong with them. But if you looked more closely, you could see they were just skin and bone. Some of the patients had a high pink colour and seemed to be putting on weight; I thought they were getting better, but in fact, it was fluid building up inside them and usually this meant their days were numbered.

It was easy to give up hope, but I tried to remain positive for Irene's sake; I wanted more than anything to go back home. It helped that the patients all supported each other; there was a great camaraderie on the ward, despite the severity of the illness. Most of the patients were ex-servicemen and there was a feeling that we faced it together, as we had done in the war. They showed the same courage, the same spirit. In many ways, having TB was like a continuation of the war; we were still fighting for our lives, but this time, the enemy was invisible bacteria inside our lungs.

Sometimes, as part of the fresh air treatment, they would push our beds outside and line us up in rows on the terrace. The nurses would bring round extra pillows and blankets and some of the patients would call out 'Will you bring me a hot water bottle?' or 'Come and tuck me in, darling.' The nurses used to take it in good part, for there were days when it seemed that the patients were only half-joking. They used to push us out in freezing temperatures, when snow lay over the grounds as the cold air was thought to be good for the lungs. We would lie there, with a view of the hills and pine trees, and we would talk to each other for company. I can still see the view from the terrace; I only have to close my eyes and I can see it: the snow-covered pines, the white expanse of the gardens, the empty chalets and the circular path leading down from the terrace which met in the middle of the gardens by a tall fir tree.

George lay in the bed next to me; when I looked across at him, his face would be red with cold. Sometimes we would be silent, we would look at the landscape in silence, but at other times, we felt the need to talk, to reminisce and recreate the past. A lot of the patients felt that, the desire to escape the present. We didn't talk much about the future, it seemed too uncertain. George told me about when he was in the airforce, about the dances they used to hold at the aerodrome and the WAAFs he'd met: 'I was a good dancer; I knew all the steps. It definitely helped where the ladies were concerned.'

As Dora went on her rounds, I saw them exchange a glance.

'What did you do before the war?'

'I was in the motor trade. I always liked messing around with cars, so it was natural to get into planes. What about yourself?'

'I'd just left school. I went straight into the navy.'

'Poor devil. You missed out on a lot.'

'Not really. I saw a lot of places I wouldn't have seen otherwise. And I'd met Irene.'

'I always wish I'd done more while my health was still good.'

'It sounds like you lived a pretty full life to me.'

'I thought so too. You don't realize how little you've done until your health is taken away from you.' I'd never heard him talk like this before; he was usually so upbeat.

'How did you find out you had TB?'

'When I was in the airforce. I'd been flying for about eight months and I was having difficulty breathing. I thought there might be something wrong with the oxygen on the plane. I had them check the tanks and the masks for leaks, but it turned out they were fine, it was my lungs that were the problem.'

'Did they ground you?'

'Not straightaway. I tried to hide it for as long as I could. Eventually, I had a medical and they found a shadow on my lungs – they sent me here.'

'You didn't want to come.'

'I'd rather have stayed in the airforce and taken my chances. I told my C.O. I could be more use to them in the air than in a hospital bed. If the disease was going to get me anyway, it didn't make any difference, but they wouldn't risk the aircraft or the safety of the crew.'

'I suppose that's understandable.'

'I miss them all. I made some good friends in the airforce. A lot of them didn't make it. Having TB probably saved my life, it's ironic really.'

'You don't need to feel guilty.'

'I know, but I felt I owed it to them to carry on, it was as if I had some obligation to the ones that didn't come back, to carry on fighting for their sake.'

I knew exactly what he meant.

'What did you want to do after the war?'

'That's the thing, I don't know what I'd have done in civilian life. I wanted to carry on flying, I would have volunteered for supply drops, airlifts, whatever. That was the most exciting time in my life – flying in the war. There was the fear, but also the exhilaration when you finished the job and came back in one piece. There was nothing that came close to it – except maybe a woman.'

'Were you ever married?'

'I was engaged once.'

'What happened to her?'

'She broke it off when she found out I had TB. Can't say I blame her really. I probably would have done the same if it had been the other way round.'

'I don't believe that.'

'What does it matter? It's all water under the bridge.' He reflected for a moment. 'Still, it could be worse. We're still here, we've got all this,' he gestured at the landscape. 'If it wasn't for this view, I'd have left long ago. I never really tire of looking at it.'

Confronted with that same view, I noticed how the landscape and colours changed with the seasons: in spring the pine trees were a dark green, whilst in winter they appeared almost bluish against the white sky. George was absorbed in the view, but I knew he was thinking of other things and we watched as the light disappeared from the sky. The bell in the tower rang to signal the end of the cure, its chimes sounding across the landscape, and the nurses and porter came out to push our beds back inside for the evening.

Another two hours lay ahead of us before lights out; it could be frustrating just lying in bed. At times, I thought I was well enough to get up, I felt like walking in the grounds, but I was still confined to bed for most of the day. 'You have to be patient with this disease,' Matron would say. 'Any exertion and you'll be back to square one.' The radio brought the crackling sound of the outside world, the news of far-away events, but it all seemed incredibly distant. I read as much as I could to keep myself occupied, to pass the waiting time – the endless succession of minutes and hours that made up the day. Every two weeks, a library lady would come round and we could choose two books from her trolley. I tried to keep myself informed, but the world, or my view of the world, had become narrower and it was difficult to relate to outside events.

We were encouraged to do light tasks, not just to pass the time, but to boost our morale, to give us a sense of purpose. I took up basket-making, threading straw. When I started, it was all so complicated and intricate that I never thought I would finish one, but we had the time to do it. I was surprised when I had completed not one, but a few dozen. I made baskets for coal, for babies, for picnics and I took one of them home when I left. Some of the other patients carved toys out of wood for the local children and the nurses would pass them on. I sometimes wonder whether they did pass them on or not or whether it was just to keep our spirits up. There was such a fear of TB at the time that I don't know if anyone would have wanted the things we made.

So life continued at a slower pace; we had our tasks to keep us occupied, but all we really wanted was to go back home. One day when we were taking the fresh air cure, I asked George whether it was possible to recover; he said it was a question of accepting the disease: 'I've seen many patients make recoveries, but a lot of them end up back here.'

'Why do they end up back here?'

'They overdo things. They think they can go back to their jobs and their old lives, but you'll never be the same as you were before.'

He pointed to one of the gardeners who was planting bulbs in the flowerbeds in front of the terrace. 'He used to be a patient, you know.'

'But he looks so well.'

'He recovered from the disease, but he couldn't cope on the outside.'

'You make it sound like a prison.'

'It's exactly like that. He got used to it, you see, the routine. They took pity on him and gave him a job here as a gardener and porter.'

'Poor fellow.'

'I hope we don't end up like that. Once I get out, I don't want to see this place again.'

'You're thinking of leaving?'

'Perhaps.'

I knew he was thinking about Dora. He felt the same loneliness we all felt. I wondered whether anything would come of it. It wasn't uncommon for relationships to develop between nurses and patients. The sanatorium could be a lonely place; after all, we were isolated, up in the hills. It wasn't only the patients who suffered; the nurses would stay for long periods in the accommodation on site and they shared our isolation.

7

The nurses weren't allowed to show any sign of affection or to favour particular patients, but it soon became apparent that something had developed between George and Dora. His face would light up whenever she appeared on the ward and he would treat her with great tenderness. 'You know the sight of you is better than all the medicines,' he would say. 'You're a perfect angel.' She would blush a fiery red, but it was clear that she returned his feelings. She had little ways of showing him affection without arousing the suspicions of the matron. She used to bring him cups of tea with extra sugar and squeeze his hand. 'You'll make someone a fantastic wife,' he told her.

At Christmas we organized a carol concert. With the help of the nurses, we decorated the dining hall; we put up tinsel and there was even a Christmas tree provided by one of the local farms. It was like before the war; it was the first celebration we'd had in that place. The nurses sang carols for an audience of patients and everyone was having a good time. Only George seemed not to be enjoying himself. Dora asked him what was wrong.

'You know what I'd really like?' he said, 'I'd like to dance. Do they have any music in this place?'

'You shouldn't overdo it,' Dora cautioned. 'You know what could happen.'

'I don't care. I'm fed up of living like an invalid. I want to dance, I want to dance with you.'

One of the nurses had some records and a player and these were brought from the nurses' home. 'You'd better keep the volume low or matron might hear,' said Dora.

'Hang matron. Tonight we're going to enjoy ourselves. Would you care for the first dance?'

'I'm not very good at dancing,' said Dora shyly.

'Don't worry, I'll teach you,' said George. 'Take my arm.'

He led her onto the floor and they took their positions. The music started and they began, tentatively at first, but she followed his lead and they grew in confidence. George was a brilliant dancer and they were soon swirling around the floor. There was applause when they finished, and some of the other patients got up to dance; it was strange to see patients dancing in the hospital. They danced all the different dances; George knew them all: the waltz, the swing, the tango, the foxtrot. Dora was smiling and they looked so happy together that I envied them and I wished Irene could have been there.

A few days later I met George in the grounds; he seemed to have something on his mind.

'I don't know if I'm doing the right thing with Dora,' he said.

'You seemed certain up till now.'

'Matron called me aside this morning when I was going for my walk – she gave me a real talking-to. She said "I don't care if you want to risk your own life, that's up to you, but I won't have you ruining the life of one of my girls." I can see her point. Dora's perfectly healthy, she has her whole life ahead of her. I don't know whether I'll be around in six months – and what if she contracted the disease, what would happen to her then?'

'Do you love the girl?'

'Yes, I do. Never thought I'd fall in love in a place like this. It's not really conducive to romance, is it? Bedpans and sputum cups. What do you think I should do?'

'Well you could both live another fifty years and never be as happy as you are now. I think you have to take what opportunities you can to be happy.'

Over the next few weeks, things moved quickly and George announced his engagement to Dora. The matron was furious at first and brought the matter to the attention of the medical superintendent. Dora was threatened with dismissal, but George said he would discharge himself first to protect her. He was called in to see the superintendent who said that George would be refused treatment if he suffered a relapse. But he had made up his mind; once he decided on a course of action, there was no turning back. He had a very strong will and the staff eventually accepted his decision as final. No action was brought against Dora and some of the medical staff even congratulated them on their coming wedding.

Before he left, we walked one last time around the grounds. Spring had come and the first flowers were out. We walked around the circular path and looked back at the gables and the belltower outlined against the sky.

'I'll miss this place in a funny sort of way,' said George. 'And some of the people.'

'Spare a thought for us occasionally when you're living the high life.'

'Don't worry, you'll be out soon. You're a survivor. I knew it the first day you came here.'

The prospect of a wedding had sent a wave of excitement through the wards of the sanatorium and there was an atmosphere of celebration that even softened Matron's heart and she gave the couple her blessing: 'You're a lucky man and don't you ever forget it.' George had called in a favour from one of his friends in the motor trade and he had arranged for a Bentley to pick them up. It was a beautiful car painted in blue and silver – it had been decked with white ribbons. Just before they left, George handed me a present which had been gift-wrapped. 'Something to bring you luck,' he said. They got in and Dora tossed the bouquet in the direction of the other nurses. We were sad to see them go, they'd brought life to the place that was as welcome as it was unfamiliar. It gave us all hope. The car made a wide sweep of the drive and the assembled staff and patients waved to the happy couple as it disappeared through the gates. I thought of Irene and I too longed to walk through those gates where I'd been brought by ambulance over two years before.

It was a different place when George and Dora left – the atmosphere had changed. Their romance had given some kind of hope to the patients and brought life to the ward, but they had taken this with them when they left. We faced long mornings and afternoons in bed, staring out of the windows at the swaying pines. Irene brought me a calendar with beautiful pictures and I would tick off the days until my next X-ray and the possibility that my lungs were clear. The tests came and went and time passed and still there was no improvement. But I was able to get up now and walk around, the medical superintendent set light exercise for me. I could walk in the grounds, along the paths, and once I even got as far as the main gates. They were closed and I stood there for a while looking through the scrolled iron railings. A horserider passed on the main road; I raised my hand in greeting, but he rode past as if I were invisible. It would be easy, I thought, to leave, to walk through the gates, but where would I go, what would I do? I couldn't go home, I couldn't risk giving them the disease. After a while I turned and went back to the ward.

8

'What was it that George gave you?' Irene asked when I told her the story.

'A rabbit's foot.'

'A rabbit's foot!?'

'Yes, it was his good luck charm – he told me once that he'd taken it with him on every mission he'd flown. There was a card inside the box: 'It never let me down – you need it now more than I do.'

And it seemed to work – it took a good many months – but slowly, I began to recover and finally, I was cleared to go home.

It would have been the perfect happy ending, had it not been for something I'd overheard in my last weeks at the sanatorium. I knew that having Irene come to visit me had caused not a little jealousy among some of my fellow inmates – those without wives or girlfriends or worse, whose partners had deserted them once they'd been diagnosed. Now they were to have their revenge.

Irene had been to visit me – she'd arrived earlier than usual: a little out of the ordinary – you could set your watch by the buses in those days, especially out in the country where there was hardly any traffic – but I hadn't really given it a second thought.

Then, after she'd gone home, I was walking among the hedges which were kept so trim by the small army of gardeners recruited from among the patients. It was then I heard two of them laughing: 'You were right about that girl, Fred – saw her getting out of some bloke's car just down the road from the main gates …'

And I knew they were talking about Irene.

Part VI:

March 1970 – September 1973

1

Before she went back to university, Sarah had said, 'You should talk to Mom, tell her what you told me.'

'Do you think it will make a difference?'

'I don't know, but you should talk to her anyway.'

The truth was that Irene and I were leading separate lives by then: we lived together under the same roof, saw each other nearly every day, but that was as far as it went – I knew that she'd stayed mainly for the sake of our daughter. And now Sarah had left home, I was afraid she'd leave me.

I knew she was still seeing Frank – it had been going on for years, probably the whole time I was in the sanatorium. But I never asked her about it except once: the night she came back after Sarah had the nosebleed – I'd had it out with her. If you can destroy someone with words, then that's what we did to each other and when it was over, I thought, 'There's no way we can go on after that.' I'd even told her to leave, given her the choice – why hadn't she taken it?

But later, I was glad she'd stayed – even if she didn't love me.

For many years, it had been like that, but recently, she'd surprised me: she'd been more affectionate.

One night, I'd come home late from locking up the school after a do; she'd run a bath for me and washed my hair. I was still self-conscious about the scarring and covered the one side of my chest with my arm – she'd noticed and said:

'You don't need to worry about that anymore.'

Later, when she'd gone down, I examined my chest in the mirror, there were little flaps of skin – 'nodules' the doctor had called them. And I thought, 'Maybe I'd better go on that trip with Sarah before it's too late.'

2

Another year passed: Sarah had almost finished her studies and for a while, things had been better between me and Irene. We'd even been to a dance. The occasion was George and Dora's wedding anniversary; against all the odds, he'd survived. There were a few faces I recognized – some of Dora's colleagues from the sanatorium, even another 'ex-inmate' as George liked to call us:

'I see you've joined the SS.'

'The what?'

'Sanatorium Survivors. A very select group – not many of us left.' He still had his old sense of humour and I was glad to see him again.

They played some of the old songs and when the opening bars of 'Moonlight Serenade' came on – that tremulous melody that was so evocative of wartime dances – couples took to the floor. I was about to ask Irene, but she shook her head: 'I can never dance when they play that one.' And then I remembered, it had been Geoff's favourite, too.

As usual, male dance partners were in short supply, and one of Dora's friends asked me to dance.

'You haven't changed a bit, you know,' she told me. 'Still with the love of your life.'

It was a ladies excuse me and I felt Irene's hand on my shoulder:

'Having a good time, then, are you?'

'Yes, I am actually. Are you jealous?'

'*No.*'

Yes, things seemed to be improving between us.

And then, one night after closing the school, I'd walked down the road and seen Frank's car parked outside our house.

The light was on in the living room window and I could hear their voices through the glass. I stood there for a moment, hesitating. 'You could just burst in on them,' I thought, 'that's what most men would do. Why do I feel like I'm the one who should be sneaking around?'

As soon as the key turned in the lock, the voices stopped; inside, there was a strange atmosphere, as if someone had died, like when there'd been a bomb during the Blitz – you hear the explosion followed by an awful silence.

Irene was standing there, he was there too; for a few moments he couldn't look me in the eye.

As if she knew what was coming, Irene had raised her hand, but I felt my mouth go dry:

'Get out, I don't care anymore that you see each other, just get out, both of you.'

'I'm sorry, I was just leaving. It's my wife, Ann, you see,' he was struggling to get the words out. 'She's had a heart attack. I'm going now, I came to tell Irene, that's all.'

It was so far from what I'd expected him to say that for a moment I was lost for words. Finally, I said: 'I'm sorry, I wouldn't have shouted if I'd known, but I still think you'd better leave.' And I saw for the first time that he was no longer the young man we'd met on that holiday; he'd aged terribly.

Irene showed him to the door – I couldn't make out what they were saying, but I could guess.

'I suppose you'll be moving in together now,' I said when she returned.

'What a thing to say – his wife's just died.'

'Well are you – are you moving in with him?'

'Of course I'm not.'

'I'm tired of this. I'd rather you told me the truth for once. Why did you marry me? Why did you agree in the end?'

'I had nowhere to go – I'd had a terrible row with my stepfather. I told him I couldn't live there anymore and he threw me out – slammed the door in my face.'

'Why didn't you tell me if you didn't love me?'

'But I did love you – I do love you … when you were ill, I thought you were going to die. I had no one to talk to – when they told me Sarah had TB, I didn't know what to do – I just needed someone to talk to. I couldn't talk to my mother – she had to do what Worthy told her – and your mother never liked me – she always thought I was carrying on behind your back.'

'Well she was right, wasn't she?'

'But it wasn't like that – not in the beginning. I know what you're thinking – what you've always thought – but you're wrong.'

'I've spent my whole life loving you, but I've never been able to trust you. I've seen other men look at you. Even my own brother.'

'Nothing ever happened between me and Geoffrey.'

'I never said it did.'

'But you always thought it, didn't you? Your mother did too.'

'He had your photo – no other photos – and Mother knew that too. That's why she'd hidden his things away.'

'You weren't here, that last night when he went away. He seemed to know he wouldn't be coming back. Of course I gave him my photo. Think about it – and you'll be glad I did.'

I did think about it – when Irene had gone to bed, I thought about Geoff travelling back to Yorkshire, alone, afraid. That photo must have been a comfort to him, something to hold onto – I knew this because I'd kept a photo of Irene in my wallet all through the war and by my bed when I was ill with the TB – I remembered what it had meant to me. There were times in the sanatorium when I thought 'I'm not going to make it out of here.' But Irene's photo had given me hope.

And I found I wanted him to have that photo. All along, I'd been afraid for the wrong reasons – but I'd realized too late.

3

'Shut the bloody door!' the landlord of the Holly Bush shouted.

'Shut it yourself,' said Geoff. That's it, I thought, we're going to get slung out, but the landlord just laughed – a rasping, throaty laugh that rattled in his chest.

'What are you having?' said Geoff. 'Not that there's much of a choice.'

Behind the bar were racks of empty bottles that had dispensed their last drop months, maybe years ago. I turned to look at the chalkboard and saw a strangely disfigured hand on the bar – I knew even before I looked up that it was Worthy, Irene's stepfather.

His back was to me, but he suddenly turned and nodded.

'This your brother, then?'

He'd hardly spoken two words with me since I'd been going out with Irene, and for a moment, my mind was a blank, but Geoff jumped in and said: 'Let me buy you a drink, Mr Johnson.'

I could see him taking Geoff in, sizing him up. The RAF uniform. And suddenly, he seemed to relax – he was more at ease than I'd ever seen him.

He didn't say that much – Geoff led the conversation – but I could tell he was impressed and that rankled with me a little bit. The ease with which Geoff impressed everyone – even, I suspected, Irene.

They seemed to be hitting it off, so I left them to it. Maybe it was the fact that I didn't have a uniform of any kind that lowered me in the old man's eyes, I don't know. He knew I was training for the Merchant Navy, but it didn't seem to cut much ice. And it wasn't just him: when I was walking round Smethwick, girls would look at me in a funny way – if they'd had a white feather on them, I'd probably have got one.

I chatted to the barmaid for a while – I'd been at school with her sister – and when I looked back, I saw the old man shaking Geoff's hand before making his way to the door.

'He's not a bad old chap,' said Geoff as we carried our drinks to a table. 'He has lost a son, you know.'

'I know, it's just that Irene doesn't get on with him – and he never speaks to me. You seem to be the exception – he'd probably rather have you for a son-in-law.'

Geoff looked at me like he did when I was joking, then saw that I wasn't.

'Son-in-law? When did you decide all this?'

'When I first met her I suppose.'

'Shouldn't you be playing the field a bit first? You're only young once, you know.'

'I've never met anyone like her, that's all.'

'My God, it is serious. Who'd have thought my younger brother would beat me to the altar? Well, I can't fault your choice.'

'Listen, I've been wanting to talk to you. I'm just worried if anything happens to me, she hasn't really got anybody that bothers about her. You would try and help her out, wouldn't you? There's no one else I can ask.'

'You're a cheery sod, aren't you? Nothing's going to happen to you.'

'You don't know that. I just want you to promise me that you'd try to look after her.'

'Course I'd look after her. Best-looking girl at the dance. I might have had a go myself if you hadn't got there first. Don't look at me like that – I'm only joking. Come on, get the round in. It might be the last drink you ever buy me.'

Sarah looked away from me. 'He loved Mom, didn't he?'

'Yes, he did. And for years I thought she loved him. I loved them both. But I couldn't forgive either of them.'

'Dad, you've had an awful time, you shouldn't blame yourself.'

'No, but it's difficult not to … I came back and he didn't.'

'It wasn't anyone's fault. It was the war.'

'I see that now, but I didn't then.'

Now, driving through Northern France with my daughter on the way to see Geoff's grave, it seemed clearer than ever. A landscape littered with white headstones. It made me think about old Worthy – why he'd ended up like he was. And I'd become the same as him – in trying to forget the past, I'd lost part of myself.

As if reading my thoughts, Sarah said: 'Poor old Worthy. I know you didn't like him, but he was always kind to me. I knew nothing about his past back then – or the war – I think he found it easier to talk to me, because I was a child.'

'Your Uncle Geoff liked him too. You remind me of him in lots of ways. He was usually right about people.'

By midday, we'd reached Amiens, where we stopped for a break. I was glad Sarah had done some of the driving – I was feeling exhausted.

We parked in a side street behind the station – it was new and drab, like the buildings they'd thrown up in Coventry after the war. Later, browsing in a souvenir shop, Sarah found an old postcard of the original Gare du Nord – a grand railway station of the nineteenth century. It must have been the same at Longueau – that was the name of the railway junction to the southeast of the city that Geoff and his crew had been sent to bomb on that tragic night. He'd been shot down about 30km to the south – they must have dropped their bombs, I thought, and been turning for home …

That the cathedral was still standing – in the midst of those targets – was testament to the skill, the accuracy of the airmen. It was a huge Gothic building, its metal spire slightly twisted: 'Was that one of the last things you saw?' I thought to myself, remembering that Geoff had told me that they used such buildings as landmarks.

We found a phone box and Sarah called Irene to tell her we'd arrived safely. She passed me the phone and I told her she was right, that it was easier with just Sarah; it had been good for us to have some time together to make up for all the times I wasn't there.

We headed south towards Beauvais on the Rue de Paris, passing through the outskirts, and I was surprised at how quickly it all became countryside again. I drove, while Sarah called out directions.

On a winding road, we passed through small, lifeless villages; everyone seemed to be indoors. We pulled up by a red barn and studied the map – it seemed like we'd come to a dead-end. Ahead of us was a field strung with telephone wires, sagging under the weight of the crows perched on top.

'I think we've missed it,' I said.

'No,' said Sarah, 'there should be another turn.'

And there was: when we passed the barn, there was a sign with the name that had haunted me for years: 'Thieux' – the village where he was buried.

There was no hill to break the horizon, flat fields, and a massive expanse of sky, an empty sky, empty of everything except the storm clouds. There would have been nowhere to hide that night, and it was in one of those fields, I thought, that their plane must have come down.

Part of me had been dreading it – reaching that village. I don't know what I'd been expecting – the mangled wreckage of a plane? – but it was nothing like that: a few cottages, some farm buildings and a small timber-frame church.

We struggled at first to find the cemetery; the church was no longer used by the look of it – some of the roof tiles had fallen off and were lying around. There was no one around to ask. So we followed the road out of the village and then we found it; it was a small enclosure out among the fields, with a low wall, you could barely see it above the yellow crop – only a rusting iron cross in the middle.

The graves of Geoff and his companions were just to the right of the entrance, by the wall. A large gravel plot with the five Imperial War Graves headstones: Geoff's was second from the left. In front, I was startled to see his picture – it was the same portrait we had at home: small photos of each airman had been enameled onto a marble plaque. I vaguely remembered Mother saying she'd sent a copy to the French family – the Resistance leader who'd arranged the funeral – but I had no idea they'd made a memorial. And it was a comfort in some way to know that visitors to the cemetery would be able to put a face to the names on the headstones.

It was such a peaceful spot, surrounded by fields – the opposite of everything that had brought him to that final place. I knew that he'd have wanted to be buried with his comrades – the friends he'd mentioned in his letters – but I also felt there was something senseless about it – no way of explaining how he'd ended up there, so far from home.

'Just twenty,' said Sarah. 'When you see it, on the gravestone, it makes it worse somehow.'

I knew what she meant. Twenty years old. Seeing it on the grave gave it some terrible finality. He would never go beyond that age, and I thought of all the things he had missed: he would never marry, never see our daughter, never have children of his own.

Sarah placed the flowers we'd brought beside some bluebells which someone had left.

'At least we know where he is, Dad – and what happened to him.'

I nodded. 'I just wish I'd said a proper goodbye to him – that's what hurts the most. When I used to see him off at the station, I would try to keep things as light as possible – we used to rib each other, we never acknowledged the possibility that he might not come back. And I often wonder whether he realized how much we all loved him.'

'I'm sure he did.'

'I hope you're right.'